WHO'S WHO IN THE MOTION PICTURE INDUSTRY

CINEMATOGRAPHERS
DIRECTORS
PRODUCERS
WRITERS
STUDIO EXECUTIVES

With Special Section
on Movies for Television

Second Edition — 1982

Packard Publishing
Beverly Hills, California

Inquiries should be addressed to Packard Publishing, 120 S. Reeves Drive, Beverly Hills, CA 90212.

Who's Who in the Motion Picture Industry is published annually by Packard Publishing.

Reasonable effort has been made in the accurate compilation of information contained in this publication; the publisher, however, assumes no liability for errors or omissions.

ISBN 0-941710-01-7

LIBRARY OF CONGRESS CATALOG
CARD NUMBER: 81-64574

TABLE OF CONTENTS

ACKNOWLEDGMENTS

This edition of Who's Who in the Motion Picture Industry has undergone several changes since the first edition. First of all, Who's Who is approximately 30% larger than last year, incorporating both new information and more credits for those persons previously listed. Each section has been substantially expanded with additional listings of directors, producers, and screenwriters. The Motion Picture Industry section has been expanded to include cinematographers. One of our objectives is to provide the reader with as much information as possible, and with the current edition we believe we have been successful.

The preparation of each edition of this book is not an easy task. There is a tremendous amount of research, information gathering, and compilation. The information contained herein, particularly the categories of studio and production company personnel, constantly changes. Since last years edition, two of the seven major studios and three of the larger production companies have been completely re-organized as far as their executive management. There have been substantial changes in the executive rosters of many of the other indepedent production companies. This is just the nature of the business.

Add to these possible situations which generate constant changes, and after all this current information is compiled, there is the job of assembling it in a manner that presents it in a clear, convenient form to you, the reader. All of this also lends credence to the old saying, "You can't tell the players without a scorecard." And Who's Who is your personal scorecard.

The following persons and organizations have all contributed to making this edition of Who's Who possible.

Many studios and film production companies have assisted in keeping us current on their executives and production people, as well as filmmakers in residence on their studio lots. Among those I would like to thank are Cheryl Boone of Simon/Reeves/Landsburg Productions, Gregg Brown of Edward R. Pressman Productions, Barbara Brogliatti of Embassy Television, Eileen Cimorell and William Self of CBS Theatrical Films, Edward Crane of Embassy Pictures, Phyllis Gardner of Metro-Goldwyn-Mayer Film Co., Bret Garwood of Aaron Spelling Productions, Richard Ingber of Twentieth Century-Fox, Maida Henderson-Pratt of Gloria Monty Productions, Allison Jackson of Paramount Pictures, Barry Jossen of the Konigsberg Co., Peter C. Kells of Columbia Pictures, Lloyd Leipzig and Burt Ford of Filmways Pictures, Susan Leh of Marble Arch Productions, Erwin Okun of Walt Disney Productions, Faryl Reingold of Twentieth Century-Fox Television, Michelle Stinson and June Callaghan of Universal Pictures, and Marisa O'Neil of Warner Bros.

Other individuals who deserve a special thanks are artist and designer Susan Aiello, film columnist and writer Bruce Burke, publishing consultant Mel Brown, writer and critic Judith Crist of TV Guide, Mary Colvig, Ian Brodie, David Norwood and Colin Penno of the Topanga Messenger, Patty Armacost and Mike Maginot of the American Cinematorgraphers Society, artists' agents John Gaines, Marvin Moss, and Robert Stein, Jan Jones of CBS Studio Center, Bari Schwartz of the Writers Guild of America-West, David Wisely of Hanson & Schwam, and special friends, Herb Edelman, Sylvan Markman, Mark McGovern, Peter Reill, Bob Sanchez, and Tony Zapata.

HOW TO USE THIS BOOK

Who's Who is divided into two main sections: "Motion Pictures," which are feature films made for theatrical release, and "Motion Pictures for Television," which are films made exclusively for television, often referred to as movies of the week.

Under the theatrical motion picture section are listings for those individuals and their credits done exclusively for release to the theaters. Also listed are "Studio Executives" and "Production Company Executives."

Under "Motion Pictures for Television" are listings for individuals and their films done exclusively for that medium. The executive personnel at the three major networks are also listed as they participate with the studios and production companies in producing and developing movies and other long form entertainment for television.

The Studios and many of the production companies work in both the theatrical and television movie area. Many directors, producers, and writers have credits in both areas as well, and therefore have listings in more than one section of this book. When an individual has credits listed elsewhere, the notation "see also Directors" or "see also Producers, Movies for Television" will enable you to find their appropriate listing in that category. Also refer to the index.

Every effort has been made to insure that the information contained in the following pages is correct. Please note: Due to the fact that persons working in the industry are constantly moving, some of the addresses and telephone numbers may have changed by the time this edition has gone to press. Also, directors and writers frequently change agents and this should be taken into account. Because Who's Who in the Motion Picture Industry is an annual publication, all listings are updated and appropriate changes are made for the next edition.

PREFACE

Within the pages of this book are found the names of a select group of people. They represent a certain type of individual who is unusually creative and dynamic, possessing certain qualities and talents which allow them to contribute to one of the most fascinating businesses in America, the motion picture industry.

The industry today is composed of seven major studios with headquarters and facilities in New York and Los Angeles. These account for the largest part of the industry. Around the major studios revolve the so-called mini-majors, who operate on a smaller scale and who often distribute their films under a major company's auspices.

The motion picture industry is small enough that agents, producers, writers, directors, and studio executives within the film community are likely to work with one another, often on a daily basis. Everyone pretty much knows, or knows of, everyone else. It is therefore important to know a person's accomplishments, his position or craft, and how to reach him; hence the necessity for a publication such as *Who's Who in the Motion Picture Industry*.

People in the industry move from one job to another or from one studio to another with regularity, and therefore are in a state of continual transition. For directors, writers, and producers, this is the nature of the business. And in recent years studio executives have fallen into the same pattern as the creative talent. The need to know where these individuals are currently, as well as their present position or title, explains why *Who's Who in the Motion Picture Industry* is constantly updated, revised, and published annually.

The criteria for being considered ''current'' depends upon whether a person wrote, directed, produced, or participated in a film project within the last few years from the date of publication, nominally since 1978. This is not an anthology containing formerly active individuals or past greats, though many of the persons listed rank among the great filmmakers of all time. The common factor shared by everyone listed is that they are currently active in the industry. Special effort has also been made to include those persons responsible at the studios and production companies for creative and literary affairs, i.e. story editors, as well as those working in a production capacity.

The main objective of this book is to be a current reference to aid those working in the motion picture industry in their daily work, as well as to aid film scholars in their research.

—*Rodman Gregg*

PART I

MOTION PICTURE INDUSTRY SECTION

DIRECTORS

AARON, Paul
(See also Directors, Movies for TV)
Agent: ICM
8899 Beverly Boulevard
Los Angeles, CA 90048
Telephone: (213) 550-4000

credits: A Different Story—1978, A Force of One—1979

ABRAHAMS, Jim
Paramount Pictures
5555 Melrose Avenue
Los Angeles, CA 90038
Telephone: (213) 468-5000

credits: Airplane *(with David and Jerry Zucker)*—1980

ADLER, Lou
credits: Up In Smoke—1978

ALDA, Alan
Twentieth Century-Fox TV
Productions
10201 W. Pico Blvd.
Los Angeles, CA 90064
Telephone: (213) 277-2211

credits: The Four Seasons—1981

ALDRICH, Robert B.
Business: The Aldrich Company
606 N. Larchmont, Suite 209
Los Angeles, CA 90004
Telephone: (213) 462-6511
Agent: Chasin-Park-Citron

credits: Whatever Happened to Baby Jane?—1964, The Dirty Dozen—1967, The Legend of Lylah Clare—1968, The Killing of Sister George—1968, Too Late the Hero—1969, The Grissom Gang—1971, Ulzana's Raid—1972, The Emperor of the North Pole—1974, The Longest Yard—1974, Hustle—1975, The Twilight's Last Gleaming—1977, The Choirboys—1978, All the Marbles—1981

ALLEN, Woody
c/o Rollins/Joffe/Morra/Brezner, Inc.
130 West 57th Street
New York, NY 10019
Telephone: (212) 765-9500

credits: What's Up Tiger Lily?—1966, Take the Money and Run—1969, Bananas—1971, Everything You Always Wanted to Know About Sex—1972, Sleeper—1973, Love and Death—1975, Annie Hall—1977, Interiors—1978, Manhattan—1979, Stardust Memories—1980

ALTMAN, Robert B.
(See also Producers, Screenwriters)
Agent: International Creative Mgmt.
40 West 57th Street
New York, NY 10019
Telephone: (212) 556-5600

Business: Landscape Films
12115 Magnolia Blvd., Suite 123
North Hollywood, CA 91607
Telephone: (213) 509-0259

credits: The Delinquents—1957, The James Dean Story—1957, Countdown—1968, Nightmare in Chicago—1969, That Cold Day in the Park—1969, M*A*S*H—1970, Brewster McCloud—1970, McCabe and Mrs. Miller—1971, Images—1972, The Long Goodbye—1973, Thieves Like Us—1974, California Split—1974, Nashville—1975, Buffalo Bill and the Indians, or Sitting Bull's History Lesson—1976, Three Women—1977, A Wedding—1978, Quintet—1978, A Perfect Couple—78, Health—1980, Popeye—1980

ANDERSON, Michael
Agent: Chasin-Park-Citron
9255 Sunset Blvd.
Los Angeles, CA 90069
Telephone: (213) 273-7190

credits: Private Angelo—1949, Waterfront—1950, The Dam Busters—1953,

directors, motion picture

ANDERSON, Michael, *continued*

"1984"—1954, Around the World in 80 Days—1956, Yangste Incident—1957, Shake Hands with the Devil—1959, The Wreck of the Mary Deare—1960, The Naked Edge—1962, Operation Crossbow—1966, The Quiller Memorandum—1966, The Shoes of the Fisherman—1968, Doc Savage—1973, Conduct Unbecoming—1974, Logan's Run—1975, Orca—1976, Bells—1980

ANNAKIN, Ken
Agent: Robbie Wald, FCA Agency
1800 Century Park East, Suite 1100
Los Angeles, CA 90067
Telephone: (213) 277-8422

credits: The Swiss Family Robinson—1960, The Hellions—1961, Crooks Anonymous—1962, The Longest Day (Brit. sequences)—1964, Those Magnificent Men in Their Flying Machines—1965, Battle of the Bulge—1966, The Long Duel—1967, The Biggest Bundle of Them All—1968, Those Daring Young Men in Their Jaunty Jalopies—1969, Call of the Wild—1972, Paper Tiger—1975, Cheaper to Keep Her—1981, The Pirate Movie—1982

APTED, Michael D.
Business: Universal Studios
100 Universal Plaza, Bungalow 81
Universal City, CA 91608
Telephone: (213) 508-1803
Agent: Creative Artists Agency
1888 Century Park East, Suite 1400
Los Angeles, CA 90067
Telephone: (213) 277-4545

credits: Triple Echo—1972, Stardust—1974, The Squeeze—1976, The Collection—1978, Agatha—1978, Coalminer's Daughter—1979, Continental Divide—1981

ARKIN, Alan
Business Manager: Saul B. Schneider
New York
Telephone: (212) 489-0990
Agent: Robinson & Associates
Beverly Hills, CA
Telephone: (213) 275-6114

credits: Little Murders—1971, Fire Sale—1976

ASHBY, Hal
Agent: Green & Reynolds
1900 Avenue of the Stars
Los Angeles, CA 90067
Telephone: (213) 553-5434

credits: Coming Home—1978, The Landlord—1970, Harold and Maude—1971, The Last Detail—1973, Shampoo—1975, Bound for Glory—1976, Being There—1980, Lookin' to Get Out—1982

ATTENBOROUGH, Richard (Sir)
Business: Beaver Lodge
Richmond Green
Surrey, England
Telephone: 01-940-7234

credits: Oh! What a Lovely War—1968, Young Winston—1972, A Bridge Too Far—1977, Magic—1978, Gandhi—1982

AVILDSEN, John G.
45 East 89th St., Apt. 37A
New York, NY 10028

credits: Turn On to Love—1967, OK Bill—1968, Guess What We Learned in School Today—1969, Joe—1970, Cry Uncle—1971, Save the Tiger—1972, The Stoolie—1972, W. W. and the Dixie Dance Kings—1975, Rocky—1976, Slow Dancing in the Big City—1979, The Formula—1980, Neighbors—1981

AVILDSEN, Tom
Agent: Marvin Moss
9200 Sunset Blvd., Suite 601
Los Angeles, CA 90069
Telephone: (213) 274-8483

AVILDSEN, Tom, *continued*
credits: Cheech and Chong's Things Are Tough All Over—1982

BADHAM, John
Agent: Adams, Ray & Rosenberg
9200 Sunset Blvd., Penthouse 25
Los Angeles, CA 90069
Telephone: (213) 278-3000
credits: The Bingo Long Traveling All-Stars—1976, Saturday Night Fever—1977, Dracula—1978, Whose Life Is It Anyway?—1981, Blue Thunder—1982

BALLARD, Carroll
Business: Lone Dog, Ltd.
P.O. Box 1383, San Rafael 94901
Telephone: (415) 454-5864
credits: The Black Stallion—1980, Never Cry Wolf—1982

BEATTY, Warren
(See also Producers)
Paramount Pictures
5555 Melrose Avenue
Los Angeles, CA 90038
Telephone: (213) 468-5000
credits: Heaven Can Wait *(co-directed with Buck Henry)*—1978, Reds—1981 *(Academy Award, Best Director—1981)*

BECKER, Harold
Agent: Adams, Ray & Rosenberg
9200 Sunset Boulevard, Penthouse 25
Los Angeles, CA 90069
Telephone: (213) 278-3000
credits: Taps—1981, The Onion Field—1979

BELSON, Jerry
Manager: Shapiro—West
141 El Camino Drive
Beverly Hills, CA 90210
Telephone: (213) 278-8896
credits: Jekyll and Hyde ... Together Again—1982

BENJAMIN, Richard
Agent: Phil Gersh Agency
222 North Canon Drive
Beverly Hills, CA 90210
Telephone: (213) 274-6611
credits: My Favorite Year—1982

BENTON, Robert
Agent: Sam Cohn, I.C.M.
40th W. 57th St.
New York, NY 10019
Telephone: (212) 556-6800
credits: Bad Company—1972, The Late Show—1977, Kramer Vs. Kramer—1979, Stab—[upcoming]

BERESFORD, Bruce
credits: Don's Party—1976, The Getting of Wisdom—1980, Breaker Morant—1980, Puberty Blues—1981

BIANCHI, Edward
Business: Ansel Productions, Inc.
141 Fifth Avenue
New York, NY 10010
Telephone: (212) 674-8221
credits: The Fan—1981

BILL, Tony
(see also Producers)
Business: Market Street Productions
73 Market Street
Venice, CA 90291
Telephone: (213) 396-5937
Agent: Bill Robinson and Associates
132 South Rodeo Drive
Beverly Hills 90212
Telephone: (213) 275-6114
credits: My Bodyguard—1980, Six Weeks—1982

BOGDANOVICH, Peter
Business: Moon Pictures
1015 Gayley Avenue
Los Angeles, CA 90024
Telephone: (213) 476-7695

directors, motion picture

BOGDANOVICH, Peter, *continued*
Agent: Robert Stein
Paul Kohner, Inc.
9169 Sunset Blvd.
Los Angeles, CA 90069
Telephone: (213) 550-1060

credits: Targets—1968, The Last Picture Show—1971, Directed by John Ford—1971, What's Up, Doc?—1972, Paper Moon—1973, Daisy Miller—1974, At Long Last Love—1975, Nickelodeon—1976, Saint Jack—1979, They All Laughed—1981

BOORMAN, John
Business Manager: International Business Management
Telephone: (213) 277-4455

credits: Catch Us If You Can—1965, Point Blank—1967, Hell in the Pacific—1969, Leo the Last—1972, Deliverance—1972, Zardoz—1973, Exorcist II–The Heretic—1977, Excalibur—1981

BOWERS, George
Crown International Pictures
292 S. La Cienega Blvd.
Beverly Hills, CA 90211

credits: The Hearse—1980, Body and Soul—

BREST, Martin
(See also Screenwriters)
Agent: Ufland Agency, Inc.
190 North Canon Drive, Suite 202
Beverly Hills, CA 90210
Telephone: (213) 273-9441

credits: Hot Tomorrow—1977, Going in Style—1979, War Games—1982

BRICKMAN, Marshall
(see also Screenwriters)
Agent: I.C.M.
40 West 57th Street
New York, NY 10019
Telephone: (212) 556-5600

credits: Simon—1980, Lovesick—[upcoming]

BRIDGES, James
Agent: Steve Roth
Creative Artists Agency
1888 Century Park East
Los Angeles, CA 90067
Telephone: (213) 277-4545

credits: The Babymaker—1970, The Paper Chase—1973, September 30, 1955—1978, The China Syndrome—1979, Urban Cowboy—1980, Mike's Murder—1982, Manhattan Melody—[upcoming]

BROOKS, Albert
(see also Screenwriters)
Agent: Creative Artists Agency
1888 Century Park East, Suite 1400
Los Angeles, CA 90067
Telephone: (213) 277-4545

credits: Real Life—1979, Modern Romance—1981

BROOKS, Joseph
Business: The Light & Sound Co. Inc.
41-A E. 74th St.
New York, NY 10021
Telephone: (212) 759-8720

credits: You Light Up My Life—1977, If Ever I See You Again—1978, Headin' for Broadway—1980

BROOKS, Mel
Business: Brooksfilms Limited
20th Century Fox
P.O. Box 900, Beverly Hills, CA 90213
Telephone: (213) 203-1375

credits: The Producers—1967, The Twelve Chairs—1970, Blazing Saddles—1974, Young Frankenstein—1974, Silent Movie—1976, High Anxiety—1977, History of the World–Part I—1981

BROOKS, Richard
Office: The Burbank Studios
4000 Warner Boulevard
Burbank, CA 91522
Telephone: (213) 954-3754
Attorney: Gerald Lipsky
Beverly Hills, CA
Telephone: (213) 878-4100

credits: Elmer Gantry—1960, Sweet Bird of Youth—1962, Lord Jim—1964, The Professionals—1966, In Cold Blood—1967, The Happy Ending—1969, Dollar$—1971, Bite the Bullit—1975, Looking for Mr. Goodbar—1977, Wrong Is Right—1982

BURROWS, James
Agent: The Broder/Kurland Agency
9046 Sunset Boulevard, Suite 202
Los Angeles, CA 90069
Telephone: (213) 274-8921

credits: Partners—1982

BYRUM, John
Agent: Wm. Morris Agency
151 El Camino Dr.
Beverly Hills, CA 90212

credits: Inserts—1975, Heart Beat—1979

CARLINO, John Lewis
(See also Screenwriters)
Agent: Michael Rosenfeld
Creative Artist Agency
1888 Century Park East
Los Angeles, CA 90067
Telephone: (213) 277-4545

credits: The Sailor Who Fell from Grace with the Sea—1976, The Great Santini—1980

CARPENTER, John
(See also Screenwriters)
Agent: Phil Gersh Agency
222 N. Canon
Beverly Hills, CA 90212
Telephone: (213) 274-6611

credits: Dark Star—1973, Assault on Precinct 13—1976, Someone's Watching Me—1978, Halloween—1978, Elvis—1979, The Fog—1980, Escape From New York—1981, The Thing—1982

CARRADINE, David
credits: Americana—1981

CASSAVETES, John
Agent: International Creative Management, 8899 Beverly Blvd.
Los Angeles, CA 90048
Telephone: (213) 550-4000

credits: Shadows—1960, Too Late Blues—1961, A Child Is Waiting—1962, Faces—1968, Husbands—1970, Minnie and Moskowitz—1971, A Woman Under the Influence—1974, The Killing of a Chinese Bookie—1976, Opening Night—1977, Gloria—1980

CATES, Gilbert
Business: The Cates Brothers Co.
9200 Sunset Blvd., Suite 913
Los Angeles, CA 90068
Telephone: (213) 273-7773

credits: I Never Sang for My Father—1969, Summer Wishes, Winter Dreams—1973, The Promise—1978, One Summer Love—1979, The Last Married Couple in America—1980, Oh, God! Book II—1980

CHAFFEY, Don
(See also Directors, Movies for TV)
Business: Nicolette Productions
Agent: Contemporary-Korman Agency
132 Lasky Drive
Beverly Hills, CA 90210
Telephone: (213) 278-8250

credits: Pete's Dragon—1976, The Magic of Lassie—1977, Shimmering Lights—1977, C.H.O.M.PS.—1978

directors, motion picture

CIMINO, Michael
Business: Partisan Productions
9336 West Washington Blvd.
Culver City, CA 90230
Telephone: (213) 204-4020
Agent: Stan Kamen
William Morris Agency
151 El Camino Dr.
Beverly Hills, CA 90212
Telephone: (213) 276-8087

credits: Thunderbolt and Lightfoot—1974, The Deer Hunter—1979, Heaven's Gate—1980

CLARK, Bob
Business Manager: Harold Cohen
Associated Management Co.
9200 Sunset Blvd.
Los Angeles, CA 90069
Telephone: (213) 550-0520

credits: Tribute—1980, Porky's—1982

COHEN, Larry
(see also Screenwriters)
Business Manager: Skip Brittenham
Los Angeles, CA
Telephone: (213) 552-3388

credits: Black Caesar—1972, It's Alive—1974, God Told Me To—1976, The Demon—1976, The Private Files of J. Edgar Hoover—1977, It Lives Again—1978, The American Success Company *(with William Richert)*—1978, Full Moon High—1980, The Serpent—1982

COLLINS, Robert L.
Agent: Bill Haber
Creative Artists Agency
1888 Century Park East, Suite 1400
Los Angeles, CA 90067
Telephone: (213) 277-4545

credits: Savage Harvest—1981

COPPOLA, Francis
Business: Zoetrope Studios
1040 N. Las Palmas
Los Angeles, CA 90038
Telephone: (213) 463-7191

credits: Tonight for Sure—1961, Dementia 13—1963, You're a Big Boy Now—1967, Finian's Rainbow—1968, The Rain People—1969, The Godfather—1972, The Conversation—1974, The Godfather Part II—1974, Apocalypse Now—1979, One from the Heart—1982, The Outsiders—[upcoming]

COSTA-GAVRAS, Constantin
Agent: William Morris Agency
151 El Camino Drive
Beverly Hills, CA 90212
Telephone: (213) 274-7451

credits: "Z"—1969, The Confession—1970, State of Siege—1972, Special Section—1975, Missing—1981

CRAVEN, Wesley
Agent: Marvin Moss
9200 Sunset Boulevard
Los Angeles, CA 90069
Telephone: (213) 274-8483

credits: The Last House on the Left—1973, The Hills Have Eyes—1977, Deadly Blessing—1981, Swamp Thing—1982

CRICHTON, Michael
(see also Screenwriters)
Agent: Mike Ovitz
Agent: Creative Artists Agency
1888 Century Park East, Suite 1400
Los Angeles, CA 90067
Telephone: (213) 277-4545

credits: Westworld—1973, Coma—1978, The Great Train Robbery—1979, Looker—1981, Congo—[upcoming]

CRONENBERG, David
Contact: FILMPLAN International
225 Roy Streat East
Montreal, Canada H2W 1M5
Telephone: (514) 845-5211

credits: Rabid—1979, Scanners—1981, Videodrome—1982, Fast Company, The Brood

CUKOR, George
Agent: Ben Benjamin, ICM
8899 Beverly Boulevard
Los Angeles, CA 90048
Telephone: (213) 550-4000
credits: What Price Hollywood—1932, A Bill of Divorcement—1932, Dinner at Eight—1933, Little Women—1933, David Copperfield—1934, Romeo and Juliet—1936, Sylvia Scarlett—1936, Camille—1937, Holiday—1938, The Women—1939, Susan and God—1940, The Philadelphia Story—1940, Two-Faced Women—1941, A Woman's Face—1941, Keeper of the Flame—1943, Gaslight—1944, Winged Victory—1944, A Double Life—1947, Edward, My Son—1948, Adam's Rib—1950, Born Yesterday—1950, The Model and the Marriage Broker—1951, Pat and Mike—1952, The Actress—1953, A Star Is Born—1954, The Chapman Report—1962, My Fair Lady—1964, Justine—1969, Travels With My Aunt—1972, Love Among the Ruins—1975, The Bluebird—1976, The Corn Is Green—1978, Rich and Famous—1981

CUNNINGHAM, Sean
Agent: Jeff Berg, ICM
8899 Beverly Boulevard
Los Angeles, CA 90048
Telephone: (213) 550-4000
credits: Here Come the Tigers—1978, Friday the 13th—1980, A Stranger Is Watching—1982

DASSIN, Jules
Athens, Greece
Agent: Sue Mengers, ICM
8899 Beverly Boulevard
Los Angeles, CA 90048
Telephone: (213) 550-4000
credits: Never on Sunday—1960, Topkapi—64, Survival—1968, Uptight—1968, Promises at Dawn—1970, A Dream of Passion—1978, A Circle of Two—1979

DAVIDSON, Martin
Agent: Jim Wiatt, ICM
8899 Beverly Boulevard
Los Angeles, CA 90048
Telephone: (213) 550-4000
credits: The Lords of Flatbush—1973, Almost Summer—1978, Hero At Large—1980

DeLUISE, Dom
c/o Hayes & Hume, P.C.
Beverly Hills, CA 90210
Telephone: (213) 858-2050
credits: Hot Stuff—1979

DEMME, Jonathan
Agent: Arnold Stiefel
William Morris Agency
151 El Camino Drive
Beverly Hills, CA 90212
Telephone: (213) 274-7451
credits: Caged Heat—1974, Crazy Mama—1975, Fighting Mad—1976, Citizens Band (Handle With Care)—1977, Last Embrace—1979, Melvin and Howard—1980, Swing Shift—1982

DePALMA, Brian
Business: Fetch Productions
25 Fifth Avenue, Suite 4A
New York, NY 10003
Agent: William Morris Agency
151 El Camino Dr., Beverly Hills, CA
credits: The Wedding Party—1963, Murder A La Mod—1968, Greetings—1968, Dionysus in 69—1970, Hi Mom!—1970, Get to Know Your Rabbit—1972, Sisters—1973, The Phantom of the Paradise—1974, Obsession—1976, Carrie—1976, The Fury—1978, Dressed to Kill—1980, Blow Out—1981

DEREK, John
Agent: Martin Baum
Creative Artists Agency
1888 Century Park East, Suite 1400
Los Angeles, CA 90067
Telephone: (213) 277-4545
credits: Tarzan, the Ape Man—1981

DESCHANEL, Caleb
Agent: Adams, Ray, and Rosenberg
9200 Sunset Blvd., Penthouse 25
Los Angeles, CA 90069
Telephone: (213) 278-3000
credits: The Escape Artist—[not yet released]

DONEN, Stanley
Agent: Leonard Hirshan
William Morris Agency
151 El Camino Drive
Beverly Hills, CA 90212
Telephone: (213) 274-7451
credits: On The Town—1949, Royal Wedding—1950, Deep in My Heart—1954, Seven Brides for Seven Brothers—1954, Singin' in the Rain—1951, Pajama Game—1957, Indiscreet—1958, Damn Yankees—1959, Charade—1963, Arabesque—1966, Two for the Road—1967, Bedazzled—1968, Staircase—1969, The Little Prince—1974, Lucky Lady—1975, Movie Movie—1978

DONNER, Clive
Agent: William Morris Agency
151 El Camino Drive
Beverly Hills, CA 90212
Telephone: (213) 274-7451
Home: 6 Melina Place
London, NW19SA, England
Telephone: 01-286-7170
credits: Nothing But The Best—1964, What's New, Pussycat?—1965, Luv—1966, Here We Go Round the Mulberry Bush, Alfred the Great, Rogue Male, The Three Hostages, The Thief of Baghdad,

The Nude Bomb—1980, Charlie Chan and the Curse of the Dragon Queen—1981

DONNER, Richard
Business Manager: Gelfand, Breslauer
1880 Century Park East
Los Angeles, CA 90067
Telephone: (213) 553-1707
credits: Salt and Pepper—1968, Twinky—1969, The Omen—1976, Superman—1978, Inside Moves—1981, The Toy—1982

DRAGOTI, Stan
Office: E.U.E.—Screen Gems
3701 Oak Street
Burbank, CA 91505
Telephone: (213) 954-3000
Agent: Creative Artists Agency
1888 Century Park East, Suite 1400
Los Angeles, CA 90067
Telephone: (213) 277-4545
credits: Dirty Little Billy, Love at First Bite—1978, Aura—[upcoming]

EASTWOOD, Clint
Business: The Malpaso Company
4000 Warner Blvd.
Burbank, CA 91522
Telephone: (213) 954-6000
credits: Play Misty For Me—1971, High Plains Drifter—1972, Breezy—1973, The Eiger Sanction—1974, The Outlaw Josey Wales — 1976, The Gauntlet — 1977, Bronco Billy—1980

EDWARDS, Blake
Business: Trellis Enterprises, Inc.
1888 Century Park East, Suite 1616
Los Angeles, CA 90067
Telephone: (213) 553-6741
credits: Breakfast at Tiffany's—1961, The Pink Panther—1963, A Shot in the Dark—1964, The Great Race—1964, What Did You Do in the War, Daddy?—1966, The

EDWARDS, Blake, *continued*
Tamarind Seed—1972, The Return of the Pink Panther—1974, The Pink Panther Strikes Again—1976, The Revenge of the Pink Panther—1978, "10"—1979, S.O.B.—1981, Victor, Victoria—1982

FARGO, James
Business: Lions Head Productions
c/o Kaufman & Burnstein
1900 Avenue of the Stars
Los Angeles, CA 90067
Telephone: (213) 277-1900
credits: The Enforcer—1976, Caravans—1977, Every Which Way But Loose—1978, A Game for Vultures—1979, The Jade Jungle—1981

FLEISCHER, Richard
Agent: Phil Gersh Agency
222 N. Canon Dr.
Beverly Hills, CA 90210
Telephone: (213) 274-6611
credits: Barabbas—1962, Fantastic Voyage—1966, Dr. Doolittle—1967, The Boston Strangler—1968, Che!—1969, Tora! Tora! Tora!—1970, The Last Run—1971, See No Evil—1971, 10 Rillington Place—1971, The New Centurions—1972, Soylent Green—1973, The Don Is Dead—1973, Mr. Majestyk—1974, The Spikes Gang—1974, Mandingo—1975, The Incredible Sarah—1976, The Prince and the Pauper—1977, Crossed Swords—1978, The Jazz Singer—1980, Tough Enough—1982

FONDA, Peter
Business: Pando Company, Inc.
10201 West Pico Blvd.
Los Angeles, CA 90035
Telephone: (213) 203-1846
credits: The Hired Hand—1971, Idaho Transfer—1972, Wanda Nevada—1978

FORBES, Bryan
Business: Pinewood Studios
Iver Heath, Bucks, England
Telephone: Iver 651-7000
Agent: William Morris Agency
Beverly Hills, CA
credits: King Rat—1965, The Madwoman of Chaillot—1969, The Raging Moon—1970, The Stepford Wives—1974, The Slipper and the Rose—1976, International Velvet—1978, Sunday Lovers (British segment)—1980, The Three of Us—1981

FOREMAN, Carl
Business: High Noon Productions
Universal Studios, Bldg. 507
Universal City, CA 91608
Telephone: (213) 508-3117
credits: Sun Yat Sen—[upcoming]

FORMAN, Milos
Agent: Robert Lantz
114 East 55th Street
New York, NY 10022
Telephone: (212) 751-2107
credits: The Competition, Black Peter, Loves of a Blonde—1965, The Firemen's Ball—1967, Taking Off—1971, The Decathlon (from Visions of Eight)—1973, One Flew Over the Cuckoo's Nest—1975, Hair—1978, Ragtime—1980

FOSSE, Robert
Agent: ICM, New York
Telephone: (212) 556-5600
credits: Sweet Charity—1969, Cabaret—1972, Lennie—1974, All That Jazz—1979, Star '80—[upcoming]

FRAKER, William
2572 Outpost Dr.
Hollywood, CA 90068
credits: Monte Walsh—1970, Reflections of Fear—1971, The Legend of the Lone Ranger—1980

FRANK, Melvin
Agent: William Morris Agency
151 El Camino Drive
Beverly Hills, CA 90212
Telephone: (213) 274-7451

credits: The Reformer and the Redhead—1950, Callaway Went Thataway—1951, Above and Beyond—1952, Strictly Dishonorable—1951, Knock on Wood—1954, That Certain Feeling—1956, The Court Jester—1956, The Jayhawkers—1959, Li'l Abner—1959, The Facts of Life—1960, Strange Bedfellows—1964, Buona Sera, Mrs. Campbell—1968, A Touch of Class—1973, The Prisoner of Second Avenue—1975, The Dutchess and the Dirtwater Fox—1976

FRANKENHEIMER, John
Agent: ICM
8899 Beverly Boulevard
Los Angeles, CA 90048
Telephone: (213) 550-4000

Business: John Frankenheimer Prods.
2800 Olympic Blvd., Suite 201
Santa Monica, CA 90404
Telephone: (213)

credits: The Young Stranger—1956, The Young Savages—1961, Birdman of Alcatraz—1962, All Fall Down—1962, The Manchurian Candidate—1962, Seven Days in May—1964, The Train—1964, Seconds—1966, Grand Prix—1966, The Extraordinary Seaman—1967, The Fixer—1968, The Gypsy Moths—1969, I Walk the Line—1970, The Horsemen—1970, Impossible Object—1973, 99 44/100 Per Cent Dead—1974, French Connection II—1975, Black Sunday—1977, Prophecy—1979, The Challenge—1982

FRAWLEY, James
Business: Maya Films, Ltd.
9220 Sunset Boulevard
Los Angeles, CA 90069
Telephone: (213) 275-3138

Agent: William Morris Agency
151 El Camino Drive
Beverly Hills, CA 90212
Telephone: (213) 274-7451

credits: The Christian Licorice Store—1970, Kid Blue—1973, The Big Bus—1976, The Muppet Movie—1979

FREEDMAN, Jerrold
Agent: Creative Artists Agency
1888 Century Park East, Suite 1400
Los Angeles, CA 90067
Telephone: (213) 277-4545

credits: Kansas City Bomber—1972, Borderline—1980

FRIEDKIN, William
Agent: Tony Fantozzi
William Morris Agency
151 El Camino Drive
Beverly Hills, CA 90212
Telephone: (213) 274-7451

credits: Good Times—1967, The Night They Raided Minsky's—1968, The Boys in the Band—1970, The French Connection—1971, The Exorcist—1973, Sorcerer—1977, Brinks—1979, Cruising—1980

FULLER, Samuel
Agent: Chasin-Park-Citron
9255 Sunset Boulevard
Los Angeles, CA 90069
Telephone: (213) 273-7190

credits: I Shot Jesse James—1949, Baron of Arizona—1950, Steel Helmet—1951, Fixed Bayonets—1951, Park Row—1952, Pickup on South Street—1953, Hell and High Water—1954, House of Bamboo—1955, Forty Guns—1957, Run of the Arrow—1957, China Gate—1957, Crimson Kimono—1959, Underworld, USA—1961, Merrill's Marauders—1962, Shock Corridor—1963, Naked Kiss—1964, Dead Pigeon on Beethoven Street—1970, The Big Red One—1980, White Dog—1981

FURIE, Sydney J.
Agent: Michael Marcus
Creative Artists Agency
1888 Century Park East, Suite 1400
Los Angeles, CA 90067
Telephone: (213) 277-4545
credits: The Leather Boys—1963, The Ipcress File—1965, The Appaloosa—1966, The Naked Runner—1967, The Lawyer—1969, Little Fauss and Big Halsey—1970, The Lady Sings the Blues—1972, Sheila Levine is Dead and Living in New York—1975, Gable and Lombard—1976, The Boys in Company C—1978, The Entity—1981

GAVRAS, Costa
Agent: Stan Kamen
William Morris Agency
151 El Camino Drive
Beverly Hills, CA 90212
Telephone: (213) 274-7451
credits: "Z"—1969, The Confession—1970, State of Siege—1972, Special Section—1975, Missing—1981

GILLIAM, Terry
Business: Handmade Films
26 Cadogan Square
London S.W. 1, England
Telephone: 01-581-1265
credits: Time Bandits—1981

GILROY, Frank
(see also Screenwriters)
Agent: Ziegler-Diskant, Inc.
9255 Sunset Boulevard
Los Angeles, CA 900690
Telephone: (213) 278-0070
credits: Desperate Characters—1971, From Noon Till Three—1976, Once in Paris—1978

GODARD, Jean-Luc
Office: Zoetrope Studios
1040 N. Las Palmas
Los Angeles, CA 90038
Telephone: (213) 463-7191
credits: Breathless—1960, My Life to Live—1961, Band of Outsiders—1962, Contempt—1963, A Married Woman—1964, Alphaville—1965, Masculine-Feminine—1966, Pierrot Le Fou—1966, Two or Three Things I Know About Her—1967, Weekend—1968, Wind From the East—1969, Number Two—1975, Every Man for Himself—1980
All films to date are French productions

GOLAN, Menahem
(see also Producers)
Business: Cannon Films
6464 Sunset Boulevard, Suite 1150
Los Angeles, CA 90028
Telephone: (213) 469-8124
credits: Operation Thunderbolt—1978, The Magician of Lublin—1979, Enter the Ninja—1981, Revenge of the Ninja—1982

GORDON, Steve
Agent: William Morris Agency
151 El Camino Drive
Beverly Hills, CA 90212
Telephone: (213) 274-7451
credits: Arthur—1981

GOTTLIEB, Carl
Agent: Larry Grossman
211 South Beverly Drive, Suite 206
Beverly Hills, CA 90212
Telephone: (213) 550-8127
credits: Caveman—1981

GREENE, David
Business: David Greene Productions
4225 Coldwater Canyon
Studio City, CA 91604
Telephone: (213) 766-3547
credits: The Shuttered Room, Sebastian, The Strange Affair, Godspell, Gray Lady Down—1978, Hard Country—1981

GREENWALD, Robert
(See also Directors, Movies for TV)
  Business: Moonlight Productions
  2029 Century Park East, Suite 424
  Los Angeles, CA 90067
  Telephone: (213) 552-9455
  Agent: William Morris Agency
  151 El Camino Drive
  Beverly Hills, CA 90212
  Telephone: (213) 274-7451
credits: Xanadu—1980

GROSSBARD, Ulu
  Agent: Sam Cohn, ICM
  New York, NY
  Telephone: (212) 556-5600
credits: The Subject Was Roses—1968,
True Confessions—1981

HACKFORD, Taylor
  Business: New Visions, Inc.
  c/o Wyman, Bautzer & Co.
  2049 Century Park East
  Los Angeles, CA 90067
  Agent: Creative Artists Agency
  1888 Century Park East
  Los Angeles, CA 900
  Telephone: (213) 277-4545
credits: The Idolmaker—1980, An Officer
and a Gentleman—[upcoming]

HAMILTON, Guy
  Agent: London, England
  Telephone: 01-493-1610
credits: The Intruder—1955, The Colditz
Story—1957, The Devil's Disciple—1959,
Touch of Larceny—1959, The Best of
Enemies—1962, Man in the Middle—
1964, Goldfinger—1964, Funeral in Ber-
lin—1968, Diamonds Are Forever—1969,
Live and Let Die—1971, The Man with the
Golden Gun—1973, The Mirror Crack'd—
1980, Evil Under the Sun—1982

HARDY, Joseph
(see also Directors, Movies for TV)

  Agent: Bill Haber
  Creative Artists Agency
  1888 Century Park East, Suite 1400
  Los Angeles, CA 90067
  Telephone: (213) 277-4545
credits: The Silence—1964, Doctor
Glas—1969

HARVEY, Anthony
  Agent: William Morris Agency
  151 El Camino Drive
  Beverly Hills, CA 90212
  Telephone: (213) 274-7451
credits: Dutchman—1967, The Lion in
Winter—1969, They Might Be Giants—
1975, Players—1979, Richard's Things—
1980

HEFFRON, Richard
(See also Directors, Movies for TV)
  Agent: Creative Artists Agency
  1888 Century Park East, Suite 1400
  Los Angeles, CA 90067
  Telephone: (213) 277-4545
credits: Trackdown, Fillmore, Newman's
Law, Futureworld—1975, Outlaw Blues—
1976, Fooling Around, I, the Jury—1981

HELLMAN, Jerome
(see also Producers)
  Bus.: 68 Malibu Colony Drive
  Malibu, CA 90265
  Telephone: (213) 456-3361
credits: Klondike—[upcoming]

HENRY, Buck
  Agent: ICM
  8899 Beverly Blvd.
  Los Angeles, CA 90048
  Telephone: (213) 550-4000
credits: Heaven Can Wait *(co-director
with Warren Beatty)*—1978, The First
Family—1980

HIGGINS, Colin
(see also Screenwriters)

HIGGINS, Colin, *continued*
Agent: Steve Roth
Creative Artists Agency
1888 Century Park East, Suite 1400
Los Angeles, CA 90067
Telephone: (213) 277-4545
credits: Foul Play—1978, Nine to Five—1980, The Best Little Whorehouse in Texas—1982

HILL, George Roy
Business: Pan Arts
4000 Warner Blvd.
Burbank, CA 91522
Telephone: (213) 954-6000
credits: Period of Adjustment—1962, Toys in the Attic—1963, The World of Henry Orient—1964, Hawaii—1966, Thoroughly Modern Millie—1967, Butch Cassidy and the Sundance Kid—1969, Slaughterhouse Five—1972, The Sting—1973, The Great Waldo Pepper—1975, Slapshot—1977, A Little Romance—1979, The World According to Garp—1982

HILL, Walter
(See also Screenwriters)
Agent: ICM
8899 Beverly Boulevard
Los Angeles, CA 90048
Telephone: (213) 550-4000
credits: Hard Times—1975, The Driver—1978, The Warriors—1977, The Long Riders—1980, Southern Comfort—1981, 48 Hours—[upcoming]

HILLER, Arthur
Office: 20th Century-Fox Studios
10201 West Pico Blvd.
Los Angeles, CA 90035
Agent: Phil Gersh Agency
222 N. Canon Dr.
Beverly Hills, CA 90212
Telephone: (213) 274-6611
credits: The Americanization of Emily—1965, Popi—1969, The Out of Towners—

1970, Love Story—1970, Plaza Suite—1971, The Hospital—1971, Man of La Mancha—1973, The Man in the Glass Booth—1975, The Silver Streak—1977, Nightwing—1978, The In-Laws—1979, Making Love—1982, Author! Author!—1982

HOOPER, Tobe
Agent: Agency for the Performing Arts
9000 Sunset Boulevard, Suite 315
Los Angeles, CA 90069
Telephone: (213) 273-0744
credits: Texas Chainsaw Massacre—1975, The Funhouse—1981, Poltergeist—1982

HOWARD, Ron
(See also Screenwriters)
Business: Major H Productions
5555 Melrose Avenue
Los Angeles, CA 90038
Telephone: (213) 468-5000
credits: Night Shift—1982

HUDSON, Hugh
Business: Enigma Overseas Variations
The Burbank Studios
4000 Warner Blvd.
Burbank, CA 91522
Telephone: (213) 954-3673
credits: Chariots of Fire *(Academy Award–Best Picture)*—1981, Greystroke—[upcoming]

HUSTON, John
Bus. Mgr.: Jess S. Morgan and Co.
Los Angeles, CA
Telephone: (213) 651-1601
credits: The Maltese Falcon—1941, Treasure of Sierra Madre—1948, Red Badge of Courage—1951, The African Queen—1952, The Misfits—1960, The Night of the Iguana—1964, Reflections in a Golden Eye—1967, A Walk with Love

HUSTON, John, *continued*
and Death—1969, The Kremlin Letter—1970, The Life and Times of Judge Roy Bean—1972, Fat City—1972, The Mackintosh Man—1973, The Man Who Would Be King—1975, Winter Kills—1978, Wise Blood—1980, Annie—1982

HUTTON, Brian
    Agent: ICM
    8899 Beverly Blvd.
    Los Angeles, CA 90048
    Telephone: (213) 550-4000

credits: Fargo—1964, The Warriors—1969, Sol Madrid—1967, Where Eagles Dare—1968, Kelly's Heroes—1970, Zee and Company—1970, Night Watch—1972, The First Deadly Sin—1980, High Road to China—[not yet released]

HYAMS, Peter
(see also Screenwriters)
    Agent: Leonard Hirshan
    William Morris Agency
    Beverly Hills, CA 90212
    Telephone: (213) 274-7451

credits: Goodnight, My Love—1972, Busting—1974, Our Time—1974, Peeper—1975, Capricorn One—1978, Hanover Street—1979, Outland—1981

IRVIN, John
    Agent: William Morris Agency
    151 El Camino
    Beverly Hills, CA 90212
    Telephone: (213) 274-7451

credits: The Dogs of War—1981, Ghost Story—1981

IVORY, James
    Business: Merchant Ivory Prod., Ltd.
    250 W. 57th St., Suite 1913-A
    New York, NY 10019
    Agent: Susan Smith Associates
    9869 Santa Monica Blvd.
    Telephone: (213) 277-8464

credits: The Householder—1963, Shakespeare Wallah—1965, The Guru—1969, Bombay Talkie—1970, Savages—1972, Adventures of a Brown Man in Search of Civilization—1972, The Wild Party—1975, Autobiography of a Princess—1975, Roseland—1977, Hullabaloo of Georgie and Bonnie's Pictures—1978, The 5:48—1979, The Europeans—1979, Jane Austen in Manhattan—1980, Quartet—1981

JAGLOM, Henry
    Business: Int. Rainbow Pictures
    933 N. La Brea
    Hollywood, CA 90038
    Telephone: (213) 851-4811

credits: A Safe Place—1971, Tracks—1977, Other People—1979, Sitting Ducks—1980, National Lampoon Goes to the Movies—1981

JARROT, Charles
    Agent: Wm. Morris Agency
    151 El Camino Dr.
    Beverly Hills, CA 90212
    Telephone: (213) 274-7451

credits: Anne of a Thousand Days—1970, Mary, Queen of Scots—1971, Lost Horizon—1972, The Dove—1974, The Littlest Horse Thieves—1977, The Other Side of Midnight—1977, The Last Flight of Noah's Ark—1979, Condorman—1981, The Amateur—1982

JEWISON, Norman
(See also Producers)
    Business: Bolton Films
    9336 West Washington Blvd.
    Culver City, CA 90230
    Telephone: (213)
    Agent: Wm. Morris Agency
    151 El Camino Dr.
    Beverly Hills, CA 90212

credits: 40 Pounds of Trouble—1963, The

JEWISON, Norman, *continued*
Thrill of it All—1963, Send Me No Flowers—1964, The Art of Love—1965, The Cincinnati Kid—1965, The Russians Are Coming, The Russians Are Coming—1966, In the Heat of the Night—1967, The Thomas Crown Affair—1968, Gaily, Gaily—1969, Fiddler on the Roof—1971, Jesus Christ, Superstar—1973, Rollerball—1975, F.I.S.T.—1978, And Justice for All—1979, Best Friends—1982

JOHNSON, Lamont
    Agent: John Gaines
    Agency for the Performing Arts
    9000 Sunset Blvd., Suite 315
    Los Angeles, CA 90069
    Telephone: (213) 273-0744
credits: Covenant with Death—1967, The Mackenzie Break—1970, A Gunfight—1970, The Groundstar Conspiracy—1972, You'll Like My Mother—1972, The Last American Hero—1973, Visit to a Chief's Son—1974, Lipstick—1976, One on One—1977, Somebody's Killed Her Husband—1978, Cattle Annie and Little Britches—1981

JORDAN, Glenn
    Agent: Bill Haber
    Creative Artists Agency
    1888 Century Park East, Suite 1400
    Los Angeles, CA 90067
    Telephone: (213) 277-4545
credits: Only When I Laugh—1981

KAGAN, Jeremy Paul
(See also Screenwriters)
    Agent: Adams, Ray, and Rosenberg
    9200 Sunset Blvd., Penthouse 25
    Los Angeles, CA 90069
    Telephone: (213) 278-3000
credits: Heroes—1978, The Big Fix—1979, The Chosen—1981, The Next Sting—1982

KAPLAN, Jonathan
(see also Directors, Movies for TV)
    Agent: Arnold Steifel
    The William Morris Agency
    151 El Camino Drive
    Beverly Hills, CA 90212
    Telephone: (213) 274-7451
    Bus. Mgr.: Gerwin, Jamner & Pariser
    760 North La Cienega Boulevard
    Los Angeles, CA 90069
    Telephone: (213) 655-4410
credits: Night Call Nurses—1972, The Student Teachers—1973, The Slams—1973, Truck Turner—1974, White-Line Fever—1975, Mr. Billion—1976, Over the Edge—1978

KASDAN, Lawrence
(See also Screenwriters)
credits: Body Heat—1981

KAUFMAN, Philip
    Agent: Steve Roth
    Creative Artists Agency
    1888 Century Park East
    Los Angeles, CA 90067
    Telephone: 277-4545
credits: The Great Northfield Minnesota Raid—1971, The White Dawn—1974, Invasion of the Bodysnatchers—1978, The Wanderers—1979, The Right Stuff—1983

KAYLOR, Robert
    Agent: ICM
    8899 Beverly Boulevard
    Los Angeles, CA 90048
    Telephone: (213) 653-4143
credits: Derby, Carney—1980

KAZAN, Elia
    Business Agent: 850 7th Ave.
    New York, NY 10019
    Telephone: (212) 246-9714
credits: A Tree Grows in Brooklyn—1945, The Sea of Grass—1947, Gentleman's

KAZAN, Elia, *continued*
Agreement—1947, Pinly—1949, Panic in the Streets—1951, A Streetcar Named Desire—1951, Viva Zapata—1952, Man on a Tightrope—1953, On The Waterfront—1954, East of Eden—1955, Baby Doll—1956, A Face in the Crowd—1957, Wild River—1960, Splendor in the Grass—1961, America, America—1963, The Arrangement—1969, The Visitors—1972, The Last Tycoon—1976

KELLY, Gene
Office: Zoetrope Studios
1040 North Las Palmas
Hollywood, CA 90038
Telephone: (213) 463-7191

credits: On the Town—1949, Singin' in the Rain—1952, It's Always Fair Weather—1955, The Happy Road, Invitation to the Dance—1957, Tunnel of Love—1958, Gigot—1962, A Guide for the Married Man—1967, Hello, Dolly!-1969, The Cheyenne Social Club—1970, That's Entertainment Part II—1975

KERSHNER, Irvin
Attorney: Tuck Silverberg
Mitchel, Silverberg, and Knupp
1800 Century Park East
Los Angeles, CA 90067
Telephone: (213) 553-5000

credits: The Hoodlum Priest—1961, A Face in the Rain—1963, The Luck of Ginger Coffey—1964, A Fine Madness—1966, The Flim Flam Man—1967, Loving—1970, Up the Sandbox—1972, S*P*Y*S—1974, Return of a Man Called Horse—1976, The Eyes of Laura Mars—1978, The Empire Strikes Back—1980, The Ninja—[not yet released]

KLEISER, Randal
Business: 3855 Lankershim Blvd.
North Hollywood, CA 91604
Telephone: (213) 760-3801

Agent: Joel Dean—ICM
8899 Beverly Blvd.
Los Angeles, CA 90048
Telephone: (213) 550-4000

credits: Grease—1978, The Blue Lagoon—1980

KORTY, John
(See also Directors, Movies for TV)
Business: Korty Films, Inc.
200 Miller Ave.
Mill Valley, CA 94941
Telephone: (415) 383-6900
Agent: William Morris Agency

credits: The Crazy Quilt—1966, Funnyman—1967, Riverrun—1969, Alex and the Gypsy—1976, Oliver's Story—1978

KOTCHEFF, Ted
Agent: Jeff Berg, ICM
8899 Beverly Boulevard
Los Angeles, CA 90048
Telephone: (213) 550-4000

credits: Tiara Tahiti—1962, Life at the Top—1965, Two Gentlemen Sharing—1970, Billy Two Hats—1973, The Apprenticeship of Duddy Kravitz—1974, Fun with Dick and Jane—1977, Who's Killing the Great Chefs of Europe?—1978, First Blood—1982

KRAMER, Stanley
(see also Producers)
Business: Stanley Kramer Productions, Ltd.
P.O. Box 158
Bellvue, Washington 90889
Telephone: (206) 454-1785

credits: Not as a Stranger—1955, The Pride and the Passion—1957, The Defiant Ones—1958, On the Beach—1959, Inherit the Wind—1960, Judgement at Nuremburg—1962, It's a Mad, Mad, Mad, Mad World—1964, Ship of Fools—1965, Guess Who's Coming to Dinner—1967,

KRAMER, Stanley, *continued*
The Secret of Santa Vittoria—1969, RPM—1970, Bless the Beasts and the Children—1971, Oklahoma Crude—1973, The Domino Principle—1977, The Runner Stumbles—1980

KUBRICK, Stanley
Attorney: Louis C. Blau
10100 Santa Monica Blvd.
Los Angeles, CA 90067
Telephone: (213) 552-7774

credits: Fear and Desire—1953, Killer's Kiss—1955, The Killing—1956, Paths of Glory—1957, Spartacus—1960, Lolita—1962, Dr. Strangelove, Or How I Learned to Stop Worrying and Love the Bomb—1964, "2001": A Space Odyssey—1968, A Clockwork Orange—1971, Barry Lyndon—1975, The Shining—1979

LANDIS, John
Business Offices: Universal Studios
Universal City Plaza
Universal City, CA 91608
Telephone: (213) 985-4321

Agent: Michael Marcus
Creative Artists Agency
1888 Century Park East, Suite 1400
Los Angeles, CA 90067
Telephone: (213) 277-4545

credits: Schlock—1971, Kentucky Fried Movie—1977, National Lampoon's Animal House—1978, The Blues Brothers—1980, An American Werewolf in London—1981

LEAN, David
credits: In Which We Serve (co-director with Noel Coward)—1942, This Happy Breed—1944, Blithe Spirit—1945, Brief Encounter—1945, Great Expectations—1946, Oliver Twist—1948, The Passionate Friends—1948, Madeleine—1950, The Sound Barrier—1952, Hobson's Choice—1954, Summertime—1955, The Bridge on the River Kwai—1957, Lawrence of Arabia—1962, Doctor Zhivago—1965, Ryan's Daughter—1970, A Passage to India—[upcoming]

LESTER, Richard
Business: Twickenham Film Studios
St. Margarets, Middlesex, England
Telephone: (213) 274-7451

credits: The Running, Jumping and Standing Still Film—1959, It's Trad, Dad!—1962, Mouse on the Moon—1963, A Hard Day's Night—1964, The Knack—1965, Help—1965, A Funny Thing Happened on the Way to the Forum, How I Won the War—1967, Petulia—1968, The Bed-Sitting Room—1969, The Three Musketeers—1974, The Four Musketeers—1974, Juggernaut—1974, Royal Flash—1975, Robin and Marian—1976, The Ritz—1976, Butch and Sundance: The Early Years—1979, Cuba—1980, Superman II—1981

LUCAS, George
(see also Producers)
Business: Lucasfilm, Ltd.
P.O. Box 2009
San Rafael, CA 94912
Telephone: (415) 457-5282

credits: THX 1138-1970, American Graffiti—1973, Star Wars—1977

LUMET, Sidney
Business: LAH Film Corp.
156 W. 56th Street
New York, NY 10019
Telephone: (212) 246-7171
Agent: Sue Mengers, ICM
8899 Beverly Blvd.
Los Angeles, CA 90048
Telephone: (213) 550-4000

credits: Twelve Angry Men—1957, Stage Struck—1958, That Kind of Woman—1959, The Fugitive Kind—1960, A View

LUMET, Sidney, *continued*

From the Bridge—1961, Long Day's Journey Into the Night—1962, Fail Safe—1964, The Pawnbroker—1965, The Hill—1965, The Group—1966, The Deadly Affair—1967, Bye Bye Braverman— 1968, The Appointment—1969, Last of the Mobile Hot Shots—1970, The Anderson Tapes—1971, Child's Play—1972, The Offence—1973, Serpico—1974, Lovin' Molly—1974, Murder on the Orient Express—1974, Dog Day Afternoon—1975, Network—1976, Equus—1977, The Wiz—1978, Just Tell Me What You Want—1980, Prince of the City—1981, Deathtrap—1982, The Verdict—1982

LYNCH, David
　Agent: Steve Roth/Rick Nicita
　Creative Artists Agency
　1888 Century Park East, Suite 1400
　Los Angeles, CA 90067
　Telephone: (213) 277-4545

credits: Eraserhead—1977, The Elephant Man—1980, Dune—[upcoming]

LYNCH, Paul M.
　Attorney: Bruce Singman
　Beverly Hills, CA 90212
　Telephone: (213) 276-2393
　Agent: Phil Gersh Agency
　222 N. Canon Drive
　Beverly Hills, CA 90210
　Telephone: (213) 274-6611

credits: The Hard Part Begins—1975, Blood and Guts—1978, Prom Night—1980, Humungus—1981

MAKAVEJEV, Dusan
　Agent: Robert Stein
　Paul Kohner, Inc.
　9169 Sunset Blvd.
　Los Angeles, CA 90069
　Telephone: (213) 550-1060

credits: W.R. Mysteries of the Organism—1971, Sweet Movie—1974, Montenegro—1981

MALICK, Terrence F.
　Agent: Evarts Ziegler
　Ziegler, Diskant, Inc.
　9255 Sunset Blvd.
　Los Angeles, CA 90069
　Telephone: (213) 278-0070

credits: Badlands—1973, Days of Heaven—1978

MALLE, Louis
　Business Manager: Gelfand, Breslaur
　489 5th Avenue
　New York, NY 10017

credits: Black Moon—1975, Pretty Baby—1977, Atlantic City—1981, My Dinner With Andre—1981

MALMUTH, Bruce
　Business: Soularview
　9981 Robbins Dr.
　Beverly Hills, CA 90212
　Telephone: (213) 277-4555
　Agent: Marvin Moss
　Telephone: (213) 274-8483

credits: Nighthawks—1981, The Hookey Players—[upcoming]

MANN, Daniel
(See also Directors, Movies for TV)
　Agent: Grossman-Stalmaster Agency
　8833 Sunset Blvd., Suite 100
　Los Angeles, CA 90069
　Telephone: (213) 657-3040

credits: Come Back Little Sheba—19__, About Mrs. Leslie—19__, The Rose Tattoo—1956, I'll Cry Tomorrow—1955, Teahouse of the August Moon—1956, Hot Spell—1958, The Last Angry Man—1959, The Mountain Road—1960, Butterfield 8—1960, Ada—1961, Who's Got the Action—1963, Who's Been Sleeping in my Bed?—1964, Judith—1966, For Love of Ivy—1968, A Dream of Kings—1969, Willard—1971, The Revengers—1972, Maurie—1973, Interval—1973, Lost in the Stars—1974, Matilda—1978

MANN, Delbert
(see also Directors, Movies for TV)
Agent: William Morris Agency
151 El Camino Drive
Beverly Hills, CA 90212
Telephone: (213) 274-7451
credits: Marty—1955, Bachelor Party—1957, Desire Under the Elms—1958, Separate Tables—1958, Middle of the Night—1959, The Dark at the Top of the Stairs—1960, The Outsider—1961, Lover Come Back—1961, That Touch of Mink—1962, A Gathering of Eagles—1963, Dear Heart—1964, Quick Before It Melts—1965, Mister Buddwing—1966, Fitzwilly—1967, The Pink Jungle—1968, Kidnapped—1971, Birch Interval—1976, Night Crossing—1982

MANN, Michael
(see also Screenwriters)
Agent: Jeff Berg, ICM
8899 Beverly Boulevard
Los Angeles, CA 90048
Telephone: (213) 550-4205
Business: Michael Mann Prod. Co.
1040 N. Las Palmas
Los Angeles, CA 90038
Telephone: (213) 463-7191
credits: Thief—1981

MARKOWITZ, Robert
(See also Directors, Movies for TV)
Agent: Jeff Berg, ICM
8899 Beverly Boulevard
Los Angeles, CA 90048
Telephone: (213) 550-4000
credits: Voices—1979

MARQUAND, Richard
c/o Lucasfilm, Ltd.
P. O. Box 2009
San Rafael, CA 94912
Telephone: (415) 457-5282
credits: Revenge of the Jedi—1983

MARSHALL, Garry
Agent: The Sy Fischer Co.
10100 Santa Monica Blvd., Suite 2440
Los Angeles, CA 90067
Telephone: (213) 557-0388
credits: Young Doctors in Love—1982

MAXWELL, Ron
Agent: ICM
8899 Beverly Boulevard
Los Angeles, CA 90048
Telephone: (213) 550-4000
credits: Little Darlings—1980, The Night the Lights Went Out in Georgia—1981, Dangerously—[upcoming]

MAZURSKY, Paul
Office: The Burbank Studios
4000 Warner Boulevard
Burbank, CA 91522
Telephone: (213) 954-3481
Agent: ICM, 8899 Beverly Blvd.
Los Angeles, CA 90048
Telephone: (213) 550-4000
credits: Bob & Carol & Ted & Alice—1969, Alex in Wonderland—1970, Blume in Love—1973, Harry and Tonto—1974, Next Stop Greenwich Village—1976, An Unmarried Woman—1978, Willie and Phil—1980, Tempest—1982

McEVEETY, Vincent
credits: Amy—1981

McLAGLEN, Andrew
(See also Directors, Movies for TV)
Agent: Contemporary-Korman Artists
132 Lasky Drive
Beverly Hills, CA 90212
Telephone: (213) 278-2850
credits: The Abductors—19__, McLintock—1964, Shenandoah—1965, The Rare Breed—1966, Monkeys, Go Home—1966, The Way West—1967, The Ballad of Josie—1968, Hellfighters—1969, The Undefeated—1969, Chisum—1970, Fools' Parade—1979, Something Big—1971,

directors, motion picture

McLAGLEN, Andrew, *continued*
One More Train to Rob—1971, Cahill, Mitchell, The Last Hard Men—1976, ffolkes—1980, The Sea Wolves—1981, The Swindle—[upcoming]

MEDAK, Peter
(See also Directors — Movies for TV)
   1415 North Genesee
   Los Angeles, CA 90046
   Agent: APA Agency
   9000 Sunset Blvd., Suite 315
   Los Angeles, CA 90069
   Telephone: (213) 273-0744

credits: Negatives—1968, A Day in the Death of Joe Egg—1969, The Ruling Class—1972, Ghost in a Noonday Sun—1973, Old Job—1977, The Changeling—1979, Zorro—1981

MERRILL, Kieth
   Agent: Film Artists Management
   Business: Kieth Merrill Associates
   11939 Rhus Ridge Rd.
   Los Altos Hills, CA 94022
   Telephone: (415) 656-7590

credits: The Great American Cowboy—1974, Three Warriors—1977, Take Down—1979, Harry's War—1980, Windwalker—1981

MEYER, Nicholas
(See also Screenwriters)
   Contact: International Business
         Management
   1801 Century Park East
   Los Angeles, CA 90067
   Telephone: (213) 277-4455

credits: Time After Time—1978, Star Trek II—1982, Charmed Lives—[upcoming]

MILES, Christopher
credits: Up Jumped the Swagmen—1965, A Time for Loving—19__, That Lucky Touch—19__, The Virgin and the Gypsy—1970, The Maids—1975, Priest of Love—1981

MILIUS, John
(See also Screenwriters)
   Agent: Jeff Berg, ICM
   8899 Beverly Boulevard
   Los Angeles, CA 90048
   Telephone: (213) 550-4000

credits: Dillinger—1972, The Wind and the Lion—1975, Big Wednesday—1979

MILLER, Robert Ellis
(see also Directors, Movies for TV)
   REM Company Films
   1901 Avenue of the Stars, Suite 1040
   Los Angeles, CA 90067
   Agent: Robert Stein
   Paul Kohner, Inc.
   9169 Sunset Blvd.
   Los Angeles, CA 90069
   Telephone: (213) 550-1060

credits: Any Wednesday—1966, Sweet November—1967, The Heart Is a Lonely Hunter—1968, The Buttercup Chain—1970, The Big Stick—1972, The Girl From Petrovka—1974

MINER, Steve
   Agent: Marvin Moss
   9200 Sunset Blvd., Suite 601
   Los Angeles, CA 90069
   Telephone: (213) 274-8483

credits: Friday the 13th Part 2—1981, Friday the 13th Part 3—[upcoming]

MINNELLI, Vincente E.
   Agent: The Paul Kohner Agency
   9169 Sunset Blvd.
   Los Angeles, CA 90069
   Telephone: (213) 550-1060

credits: Numerous feature films—most recent are: The Sandpiper—1965, On a Clear Day You Can See Forever—1970, A Matter of Time—1976

MOORE, Robert
   Agent: The Artists Agency
   190 N. Canon
   Beverly Hills, CA 90210
   Telephone: (213) 278-3200

MOORE, Robert, *continued*

credits: Murder by Death—1976, The Cheap Detective—1978, Chapter Two—1979

MULLIGAN, Robert
Agent: William Morris Agency
Beverly Hills, CA 90212
Telephone: (213) 274-7451

credits: Inside Daisy Clover—1966, Up the Down Staircase—1967, The Stalking Moon—1968, The Piano Sport—1969, Good Times, Bad Times—1970, The Pursuit of Happiness—1970, The Summer of '42, The Other—1972, The Nickel Ride—1974, Bloodbrothers—1978, Same Time Next Year—1978, Kiss Me Goodbye *(also producer)*—1983

MUTRUX, Floyd
Office: The Burbank Studios
4000 Warner Boulevard
Burbank, CA 91522
Telephone: (213) 954-3481
Agent: ICM
8899 Beverly Boulevard
Los Angeles, CA 90048
Telephone: (213) 550-4000

credits: Dusty and Sweets Mcgee—1971, Aloha Bobby and Rose—1975, American Hot Wax—1978

NEAME, Ronald
2317 Kimridge Rd.
Beverly Hills, CA 90212
Agent: John Gaines
Agency for the Performing Arts
Telephone: (213) 273-0744

credits: Take My Life—1950, The Golden Salamander—1951, The Promoter—1952, The Million Pound Note—1953, The Man Who Never Was—1954, Windom's Way—1957, The Horse's Mouth—1958, Tunes of Glory—1960, Escape From Zahrain—1961, I Could Go On Singing—1962, The Chalk Garden—1963, Mr. Moses—1964, Gambit—1966, The Prime of Miss Jean Brodie—1968, Scrooge—1970, The Poseidon Adventure—1972, The Odessa File—1974, Meteor—1978, Hopscotch—1980, First Monday in October—1981

NEEDHAM, Hal
Bus. Mgr.: Laura Lizer and Assoc.
3518 Cahuenga Blvd. West
Los Angeles, CA 90028
Telephone: (213) 876-4040

credits: Smokey and the Bandit—1977, Hooper—1978, The Villain—1979, Smokey and the Bandit II—1980, Megaforce—1982

NELSON, Ralph
Business: Rainbow Productions
1900 Avenue of the Stars, Suite 2270
Los Angeles, CA 90067
Telephone: (213) 277-1900
Agent: Chasin-Park-Citron Agency
9255 Sunset Blvd.
Los Angeles, CA 90069
Telephone: (213) 941-8150

credits: Requiem for a Heavyweight—1962, Lilies of the Field—1963, Soldier in the Rain—1963, Father Goose—1964, Counterpoint—1967, Charly—68, Tick, Tick, Tick—1969, Soldier Blue—1970, Flight of the Doves—1971, The Wrath of God—1972, The Wilby Conspiracy—1975, The Embryo—1976, A Hero Ain't Nothin' But a Sandwich—1977

NICHOLS, Mike
Attorney: Marvin B. Meyer
Rosenfeld, Meyer & Susman
Beverly Hills, CA
Telephone: (213) 858-7700
Agent: ICM New York, Sam Cohn
Telephone: (212) 556-6810

credits: Who's Afraid of Virginia Woolf?—1966, The Graduate—1967, Catch 22—1970, Carnal Knowledge—1971, The Day of the Dolphin—1973, The Fortune—1975, Chain Reaction—[upcoming]

NOSSECK, Noel
(see also Directors, Movies for TV)
  Agent: Chasin-Park-Citron
  9255 Sunset Boulevard
  Los Angeles, CA 90069
  Telephone: (213) 273-7190
credits: Best Friends—1975, Young
Blood, Dreamer—1979, King of the Mountain—1981

OLIANSKY, Joel
  Agent: Adams, Ray & Rosenberg
  9200 Sunset Blvd., Penthouse 25
  Los Angeles, CA 90069
  Telephone: (213) 278-3000
credits: The Competition—1980

PAKULA, Alan J.
  Business: Gus Productions
  10889 Wilshire
  Los Angeles, CA 90024
  Telephone: (213) 208-3046
  Agent: Stan Kamen
  William Morris Agency
  Beverly Hills, CA 90212
  Telephone: (213) 274-7451
credits: The Sterile Cuckoo—1969,
Klute—1971, Love, Pain and the Whole
Damn Thing—1972, The Parallax View—
1974, All the President's Men—1976,
Comes a Horseman—1978, Starting
Over—1979, Rollover—1981, Sophie's
Choice—1983

PALTROW, Bruce
  Office: MTM Enterprises
  4024 Radford Avenue
  Studio City, CA 91604
  Telephone: (213) 760-5000
credits: A Little Sex—1982

PARKER, Alan
  Agent: William Morris Agency
  151 El Camino Dr.
  Beverly Hills, CA 90212
  Telephone: (213) 274-7451
credits: No Hard Feelings, The Evacuees,
Bugsy Malone—1976, Midnight Express—1978, Fame—1980, Shoot the
Moon—1982, Pink Floyd: The Wall—1982

PASSER, Ivan
  Agent: Robert Stein
  Paul Kohner, Inc.
  9169 Sunset Boulevard
  Los Angeles, CA 90069
  Telephone (213) 550-1060
credits: A Boring Afternoon—1964, Intimate Lighting—1966, The Legend of
Beautiful Julia—1968, Born to Win—
1971, Law and Disorder—1974, Silver
Bears—1978, Cutter's Way—1981

PEARCE, Richard
  Agent: William Morris Agency
  1350 Avenue of the Americas
  New York, NY 10019
  Telephone: (212) 586-5100
credits: Heartland—1981

PECKINPAH, Sam
  Agent: Chasin-Park-Citron
  9255 Sunset Blvd.
  Los Angeles, CA 90069
  Telephone: (213) 273-7190
credits: The Deadly Companions—1961,
Ride the High Country—1962, Major
Dundee—1965, The Wild Bunch—1969,
The Ballad of Cable Hogue—1970, Straw
Dogs—1971, Junior Bonner—1972, The
Getaway—1972, Pat Garrett and Billy the
Kid—1973, Bring Me the Head of Alfredo
Garcia—1974, The Killer Elite—1975,
Cross of Iron—1977, Convoy—1978, The
Osterman Weekend—[upcoming]

PEERCE, Larry
  Agent: Creative Artists Agency
  1888 Century Park East
  Los Angeles, CA 90067
  Telephone: (213) 277-4545
credits: One Potato, Two Potato—1966,
Goodbye Columbus—1969, A Separate

PEERCE, Larry, *continued*
Peace—1973, Ash Wednesday—1973, The Other Side of the Mountain—1975, Two Minute Warning—1976, The Bell Jar—1978, Why Would I Lie?—1980

PENN, Arthur
Business: Florin Productions
1860 Broadway
New York, NY 10023
Telephone: (213) 582-1470

credits: The Left Handed Gun—1958, The Miracle Worker—1962, Mickey One—1965, The Chase—1965, Bonnie and Clyde—1967, Alice's Restaurant—1969, The Highest—1973, Night Moves—1975, The Missouri Breaks—1976, Four Friends—1981

PERRY, Frank
(see also Screenwriters)
Business: Frank Perry Films
655 Park Avenue
New York, NY 10021

credits: David and Lisa—1962, Ladybug, Ladybug—1963, The Swimmer—1968, Last Summer—1969, Diary of a Mad Housewife—1970, Doc—1971, Play It As It Lays—1972, Man on a Swing—1974, Rancho Deluxe—1975, Mommie Dearest—1980, Monsignore—1982

PERSKY, Bill
Agent: Creative Artists Agency
1888 Century Park East, Suite 1400
Los Angeles, CA 90067
Telephone: (213) 277-4545

credits: Serial—1980

PETRIE, Daniel
Office: 20th Century-Fox
P.O. Box 900
Beverly Hills, CA 90213
Agent: Jack Gilardi, ICM
8899 Beverly Boulevard
Los Angeles, CA 90048
Telephone: (213) 550-4000

credits: A Raisin in the Sun—1961, The Spy with the Cold Nose—1967, The Neptune Factor—1972, Buster and Billie—1974, Lifeguard—1976, The Betsy—1977, Resurrection—1980, Fort Apache: The Bronx—1981, Six Pack—1982

PIERSON, Frank
Agent: Adams, Ray and Rosenberg
9200 Sunset Boulevard, Suite 25
Los Angeles, CA 90069
Telephone: (213) 278-3000

credits: The Looking Glass War—1969, A Star Is Born—1976, King of the Gypsies—1979

PINTOFF, Ernest
Agent: Contemporary-Korman Artists
132 Lasky Drive
Beverly Hills, CA 90212
Telephone: (213) 278-8250

credits: Jaguar Lives, Fireman, Harvey Middleman, The Shoes, Dynamite Chicken, Blade, The Interview, The Violinist, The Critic, St. Helens—1981

POITIER, Sidney
Business: Verdon Productions, Ltd.
9350 Wilshire Blvd., Suite 310
Beverly Hills, CA 90212
Telephone: (213) 274-7253
Agent: Creative Artists Agency
1888 Century Park East, Suite 1400
Los Angeles, CA 90067
Telephone: (213) 277-4545

credits: Buck and the Preacher—1970, A Warm December—1972, Uptown Saturday Night—1974, Let's Do It Again—1975, A Piece of the Action—1978, Stir Crazy—1980, Hanky Panky—1982

POLANSKI, Roman
Business Manager: Carlin Levy & Co.
265 N. Robertson
Beverly Hills, CA 90211
credits: Repulsion—1965, Cul de

directors, motion picture

POLANSKI, Roman, *continued*
Sac—1966, The Fearless VampireKillers—1967, Rosemary's Baby—1968, Macbeth—1972, What?—1973, Chinatown—1974, The Tenant—1976, Tess—1981

POLLACK, Sydney
Business Manager: Armstrong,
   Hendler & Hirsch
1888 Century Park East
Los Angeles, CA 90067
Telephone: (213) 553-0305
Business: Mirage Productions
4000 Warner Blvd.
Burbank, CA 91522
Telephone: (213) 954-1711

credits: The Slender Thread—1965, This Property Is Condemned—1966, The Scalphunters—1968, Castle Keep—1968, The Swimmer—1968, They Shoot Horses, Don't They?—1969, Jeremiah Johnson—1972, The Way We Were—1973, Three Days of the Condor—1975, The Yakuza—1975, Bobby Deerfield—1977, The Electric Horseman—1979, Absence of Malice—1981, Tootsie—1982

POST, Ted
(see also Directors, Movies for TV)
   Business: T. P. Films Ltd.
   c/o Blumenthal & Levin
   3250 Ocean Park Blvd.
   Santa Monica, CA 90405
   Telephone: (213) 452-7747

credits: Hang 'Em High—1968, Beneath the Planet of the Apes—1970, The Baby—1973, The Harrad Experiment—1973, Magnum Force—1973, Whiffs—1975, Go Tell the Spartans—1978, Good Guys Wear Black—1979

PREMINGER, Otto
   Business: Sigma Productions, Inc.
   129 E. 64th St.
   New York, NY 10021

credits: Advise and Consent—1962, The Cardinal—1963, In Harm's Way—1965, Hurry Sundown—1967, Skiddo—1968, Tell Me That You Love Me, Junie Moon—1969, Such Good Friends—1971, Rosebud—1975, The Human Factor—1979

PRESSMAN, Michael
(see also Directors, Movies for TV)
   Agent: Creative Artists Agency
   1888 Century Park East, Suite 1400
   Los Angeles, CA 90067
   Telephone: (213) 277-4545

credits: The Great Texas Dynamite Chase—1975, The Bad News Bears in Breaking Training—1977, Boulevard Nights—1979, Those Lips, Those Eyes—1980, Some Kind of Hero—1982

RAFELSON, Bob
   Business: c/o Wolff
   1400 N. Fuller Ave.
   Hollywood, CA 90046

credits: Head—1968, Five Easy Pieces—1970, The King of Marvin Gardens—1972, Stay Hungry—1976, The Postman Always Rings Twice—1981

RAMIS, Harold A.
(see also Screenwriters)
   Agent: Creative Artists Agency
   1888 Century Park East, Suite 1400
   Los Angeles, CA 90067
   Telephone: (213) 277-4545

credits: Caddyshack—1980

RASH, Steve R.
   Business: Innovisions, Inc.
   11751 Mississippi Ave.
   Los Angeles, CA 90025
   Telephone: (213) 478-3523

credits: The Buddy Holly Story—1979, Under the Rainbow—1981

REDFORD, Robert
Business: Wildwood Enterprises
4000 Warner Blvd.
Burbank, CA 91522
Telephone: (213) 843-6000
credits: Ordinary People—1980

REINER, Carl
Business: Aspen Film Society
7958 Beverly Boulevard
Los Angeles, CA 90048
Telephone: (213) 655-8950

credits: Enter Laughing—1967, The Comic—1969, Where's Poppa?—1970, Oh, God—1977, The One and Only—1978, The Jerk—1979, Dead Men Don't Wear Plaid—1982

REISZ, Karel
Agent: William Morris Agency
151 El Camino Dr.
Beverly Hills, CA 90212
Telephone: (213) 550-4000

credits: We Are the Lambeth Boys—1958, Saturday Night and Sunday Morning—1960, Night Must Fall—1964, Morgan—1966, Isadora—1966, The Gambler—1975, Who'll Stop the Rain—1978, The French Lieutenant's Woman—1981, Lydee Breeze—[upcoming]

REITMAN, Ivan
Columbia Pictures
Columbia Plaza
Burbank, CA 91505
Telephone: (213) 954-1771
credits: Meatballs—1979, Stripes—1981

REYNOLDS, Burt
8730 Sunset Blvd., Suite 201
Los Angeles, CA 90069
Telephone: (213) 652-6005
credits: Gator—1975, The End—1977, Sharky's Machine—1981

RICHARDS, Dick
Agent: Stan Kamen
William Morris Agency
Telephone: (213) 274-7451
credits: The Culpepper Cattle Company—1972, Rafferty and the Goldust Twins—1974, Farewell, My Lovely—1975, March or Die—1977, Death Valley—1982

RICHARDSON, Tony
1478 North Kings Road
Los Angeles, CA 90069
Agent: ICM
8899 Beverly Boulevard
Los Angeles, CA 90048
Telephone: (213) 550-4000

credits: Look Back in Anger—1958, The Entertainer—1959, A Taste of Honey—1961, The Loneliness of the Long Distance Runner—1962, The Loved One—1964, Mademoiselle—1965, The Sailor from Gibralter—1967, Red and Blue—1966, The Charge of the Light Brigade—1968, Laughter in the Dark—1969, Ned Kelly—1970, Hamlet—1971, A Delicate Balance—1972, Dead Certain—1974, Joseph Andrews—1977, A Death in Canaan—1978, The Border—1982, The Hotel New Hampshire[upcoming]

RITCHIE, Michael
Business Manager: Freedman, Kinzelberg and Broder
1801 Ave. of the Stars, Suite 911
Los Angeles, CA 90067
Telephone: (213) 277-0700

credits: Downhill Racer—1969, Prime Cut—1972, The Candidate—1972, Smile—1975, The Bad News Bears—1976, Semi-Tough—1977, The Island—1979, An Almost Perfect Affair—1979, Divine Madness—1980

RITT, Martin
Agent: Chasin-Park-Citron Agency
9255 Sunset Blvd.
Los Angeles, CA 90069
Telephone: (213) 273-7190

directors, motion picture

RITT, Martin, *continued*

credits: Edge of the City—1957, The Long Hot Summer—1958, Hud—1963, The Outrage—1964, The Spy Who Came in from the Cold—1965, Hombre—1967, The Brotherhood—1968, The Molly Maguires—1969, The Great White Hope—1970, Sounder—1972, Pete 'n' Tillie, Conrack—1974, The Front—1976, Casey's Shadow—1978, Norma Rae—1979, Back Roads—1981, No Small Affair—19__, Cross Creek—1982

ROEG, Nicolas
Agent: Robert Littman
409 N. Camden Drive
Beverly Hills, CA 90210
Telephone: (213) 278-1572

credits: Performance—1970, Walkabout—1971, Don't Look Now—1974, The Man Who Fell to Earth—1976, Bad Timing—1979, Eureka—1982

ROMERO, George A.
Business: Laurel Entertainment
247 Fort Pitt Boulevard
Pittsburgh, PA
Telephone: (412) 261-5589

credits: Night of the Living Dead—1968, Jack's Wife—1970, The Crazies—1974, Martin—1977

ROSENBERG, Stuart
Agent: William Morris Agency
Beverly Hills, CA
Telephone: (213) 274-7451

credits: Cool Hand Luke—1967, The April Fools—1969, Move—1970, W.U.S.A.—1970, Pocket Money—1972, The Laughing Policeman—1973, The Drowning Pool—1975, Voyage of the Damned—1976

ROSENTHAL, Rick
Agent: Phil Gersh Agency
222 North Canon Drive
Beverly Hills, CA 90210
Telephone: (213) 274-6611

credits: Halloween II—1981

ROSS, Herbert
Offices: 20th Century-Fox
10201 West Pico
Los Angeles, CA 90064
Telephone: (213) 277-2211
Agent: Stan Kamen
William Morris Agency
Beverly Hills, CA
Telephone: (213) 274-7451

credits: Goodbye Mr. Chips—1969, The Owl and the Pussycat—1970, T. R. Baskin—1971, Play It Again, Sam—1972, The Last of Sheila—1973, Funny Lady—1975, The Sunshine Boys—1975, The Seven Per Cent Solution—1976, The Turning Point—1977, The Goodbye Girl—1978, California Suite—1978, Nijinsky—1979, Pennies From Heaven—1981, I Ought to be in Pictures—1982, Max Dugan Returns—1983

RUSSEL, Ken
Agent: Ralph Mann, ICM
8899 Beverly Boulevard
Los Angeles, CA 90048
Telephone: (213) 550-4000

credits: Women in Love—1970, Tommy—1971, Liztomania—1973, Valentino—1977, Altered States—1980, The Living End—19__

RUSH, Richard W.
Business: The Film Organization
821 Stradella Road
Los Angeles, CA 90024
Agent: ICM, Los Angeles
Telephone: (213) 550-4000

credits: Too Soon To Love—1960, Of Love and Desire—1963, Thunder Alley—1966, A Man Called Dagger—1966, Fickle

Columbia Pictures

For Columbia Pictures See Page 97

RUSH, Richard W., *continued*
Finger of Fate—1966, Hell's Angels on Wheels—1967, Psych-out—1967, Savage Seven—1968, Getting Straight—1970, Freebie and the Bean—1974, The Stunt Man—1980

RYDELL, Mark
(see also Producers)
Agent: ICM, Jeff McElwaine, Jeff Berg
8899 Beverly Blvd.
Los Angeles, CA 90048
Telephone: (213) 550-4000

credits: The Fox—1968, The Reivers—1969, The Cowboys—1972, Cinderella Liberty—1974, Harry and Walter Go to New York—1976, The Rose—1978, On Golden Pond—1981, The White Hotel—[upcoming]

SANDRICH, Jay H.
Agent: Mike Ovitz
Creative Artists Agency
1888 Century Park East, Suite 1400
Los Angeles, CA 90067
Telephone: (213) 277-4545

credits: Seems Like Old Times—1980

SARGENT, Joseph
(see also Directors, Movies for TV(
Business: Joseph Sargent Productions
Metromedia Producers Corp.
5746 Sunset Boulevard
Hollywood, CA 90028
Telephone: (213) 462-7111, Ext. 1292
Agent: Shapiro-Lichtman, Inc.
2049 Century Park East, Suite 1320
Los Angeles, CA 90067

credits: To Hell With Heroes—1968, The Forbin Project—1969, White Lightning—1973, The Taking of Pelham 1-2-3—1974, MacArthur—1977, Coast to Coast—1980

SCHAEFFER, George
(see also Directors, Movies for TV)

Business: Schaefer-Karpf Productions
Warner Hollywood Studios
1041 North Formosa Avenue
Los Angeles, CA 90048
Agent: Chasin-Park-Citron
9255 Sunset Blvd., Suite 910
Los Angeles, CA 90069
Telephone: (213) 273-7190

credits: Generation—1969, Pendulum—1969, Doctor's Wives—1971, Macbeth—1971, An Enemy of the People—1976

SCHAFFNER, Franklin
Agent: Chasin-Park-Citron
9255 Sunset Blvd.
Los Angeles, CA 90069
Telephone: (213) 273-7190

credits: The Stripper—1963, The Best Man—1964, The War Lord—1965, The Planet of the Apes—1968, The Double Man—1968, Patton—1969, Nicholas and Alexander—1971, Papillon—1973, Islands in the Stream—1977, The Boys from Brazil—1978, Sphinx—1981

SCHATZBERG, Jerry
Business Manager: Bard & Kass
551 Fifth Avenue
New York, NY 10017
Telephone: (212) 599-2880
Agent: William Morris Agency
1350 Avenue of the Americas
New York, NY 10019
Telephone: (212) 586-5100

credits: Puzzle of a Downfall Child—1970, The Panic in Needle Park—1971, Scarecrow—1973, Dandy the All American Girl—1976, Sweet Revenge—1977, The Seduction of Joe Tynan—1978, Honeysuckle Rose—1980, The Duke of Deception—[upcoming]

SCHLESINGER, John
Office: 20th Century-Fox Studios
Telephone: (213) 203-3534

SCHLESINGER, John, *continued*
Agent: William Morris Agency
151 El Camino Drive
Beverly Hills, CA 90212
Telephone: (213) 274-7451
credits: A Kind of Loving—1962, Billy Liar—1963, Darling—1965, Far from the Madding Crowd—1967, Midnight Cowboy—1969, Sunday, Bloody Sunday—1971, The Longest (From Visions of Eight)—1973, The Day of the Locust—1975, Marathon Man—1976, Yanks—1979, Honky Tonk Freeway—1981, The Falcon and the Snowman—1982

SCHMOELLER, David
(see also Screenwriters)
Business: The Schmoeller Corporation
2244 Stanley Hills Drive
Los Angeles, CA 90046
Telephone: (213) 654-0748
credits: Tourist Trap—1979, The Seduction—1982, K*A*O*S—1982

SCHRADER, Paul
(see also Screenwriters)
Business Office: Universal Studios
100 Universal City Plaza
Universal City, CA 91608
Agent: Jeff Berg, ICM
8899 Beverly Boulevard
Los Angeles, CA 90048
Telephone: (213) 550-4000
Business Office: Universal Studios
credits: Blue Collar—1978, Hardcore—1978, American Gigolo—1979, Cat People—1982

SCHULTZ, Michael
Business: Crystalite Productions, Inc.
P.OP. Box 8659
San Marino, CA 91108
credits: Cooley High—1975, Car Wash—1976, Greased Lightning—1977, Which Way Is Up—1977, Sgt. Pepper's Lonely Hearts Club Band—1978, Scavenger Hunt—1979, Carbon Copy—1981, Bustin' Loose—1981

SCORSESE, Martin
Business Manager: Jay Julien
9 East 41st Street
New York, NY 10017
Telephone: (212) 697-9680
Agent: Ufland Agency, Inc.
190 North Canon Drive, Suite 202
Beverly Hills, CA 90210
Telephone: (213) 273-9441
credits: Who's That Knocking At My Door—1969, Boxcar Bertha—1972, Mean Streets—1973, Alice Doesn't Live Here Anymore—1974, Taxi Driver—1976, New York, New York—1977, The Last Waltz—1978, Raging Bull—1980, The King of Comedy—1982

SCOTT, Ridley
Agent: Ufland Agency, Inc.
190 North Canon Drive, Suite 202
Beverly Hills, CA 90210
Telephone: (213) 273-9441
credits: Alien—79, Blade Runner—1982

SIEGEL, Donald
Business Manager: Flekman, Carwell & Co.
Beverly Hills, CA 90210
Telephone: (213) 274-5847
credits: Madigan—1968, Coogan's Bluff—1968, Death of a Gunfighter—1969, Two Mules for Sister Sara—1969, The Beguiled—1971, Dirty Harry—1971, Charley Varrick—1972, The Black Windmill—1974, The Shootist—1976, Telefon—1977, Escape from Alcatraz—1979, Rough Cut—1980, It's All In The Game—1982

SILVER, Joan Micklin
Business: 600 Madison Ave.
New York, NY 10022
Telephone: (212) 355-0282

directors, motion picture

SILVER, Joan Micklin, *continued*
credits: Hester Street—1974, Bernice Bobs Her Hair—1976, Between the Lines—1977, Head Over Heels—1979

SILVERSTEIN, Elliott
Agent: Harold Cohen
credits: Cat Ballou—1965, The Happening—1967, A Man Called Horse—1970, The Car—1977

SMIGHT, Jack
Agent: Contemporary-Korman Artists
132 Lasky Drive
Beverly Hills, CA 90212
Telephone: (213) 278-8250
credits: Harper—1966, The Secret War of Harry Frigg—1967, No Way to Treat a Lady—1968, The Traveling Executioner—1969, The Illustrated Man—1969, Rabbit Run—1970, Airport 75—1975, Midway—1976, Damnation Alley—1977, Fast Break—1979, Loving Couples—1980

SPIELBERG, Steven
(see also Producers)
Office: MGM Studios
10202 West Washington Blvd.
Culver City, CA 90230
Telephone: (213) 558-5449
Agent: Guy McElwaine, ICM
Telephone: (213) 550-4000
credits: Duel—1971, Sugarland Express—1973, Jaws—1975, Close Encounters of the Third Kind—1977, "1941"—1979, Raiders of the Lost Ark—1981, A Boy's Life—1982, A Guy Named Joe—[upcoming]

STALLONE, Sylvester
(see also Screenwriters)
Agent: Creative Artists Agency
1888 Century Park East, Suite 1400
Los Angeles, CA 90067
Telephone: (213) 277-4545
credits: Paradise Alley—1978, Rocky II—1979

STEINBERG, David
Business: Reynolds-Steinberg Co.
4000 Warner Blvd.
Burbank, CA 91522
Telephone: (213) 954-6000
credits: Paternity—1981

STONE, Oliver
(see also Screenwriters)
Business: Ixtlan, Inc.
9025 Wilshire Boulevard
Beverly Hills, CA 90211
Telephone: (213) 858-1276
credits: Seizure—1974, The Hand—1981

STRICK, Joseph
Business: Trans-Lux Corp.
625 Madison Ave.
New York, NY 10022
Telephone: (212) 751-3110
credits: The Savage Eye—1959, The Balcony—1964, Ulysses—1967, Tropic of Cancer—1969, Road Movie, 1973, A Portrait of the Artist as a Young Man—1977, Never Cry Wolf—1981

STURGES, John
Business: The Alpha Corp.
13063 Ventura Blvd., Suite 202
North Hollywood, CA 91604
Telephone: (213) 788-5750
credits: Bad Day at Black Rock—1955, The Old Man and the Sea—1958, Gunfight at the OK Corral—1959, Magnificent Seven—1960, The Great Escape—1963, The Hour of the Gun—1967, Ice Station Zebra—1968, Marooned—1969, Joe Kidd—1972, McQ—1974, The Eagle Has Landed—1977

SZWARC, Jeannot
Business: Terpsichore Productions
10100 Santa Monica Blvd., Suite 2500
Los Angeles, CA 90067
Telephone: (213) 553-8200
credits: The Extreme Close-Up—1973,

SZWARC, Jeannot, *continued*
Bug—1975, Jaws II—1978, Somewhere in Time—1980, Enigma—1981

TAYLOR, Don
  Agent: Phil Gersh Agency
  222 North Canon Drive
  Beverly Hills, CA 90210
  Telephone: (213) 274-6611
credits: Jack of Diamonds, Five Man Army, Escape From Planet of the Apes, Tom Sawyer, Echoes of a Summer, Great Scout and Cathouse Thursday—1979, The Island of Dr. Moreau—1978, The Final Countdown—1980

THOMPSON, J. Lee
  Agent: Chasin-Park-Citron
  9255 Sunset Boulevard
  Los Angeles, CA 90069
  Telephone: (213) 273-7190
credits: Tiger Bay—1959, I Aim at the Stars—1960, The Guns of Navarone—1961, Cape Fear—1964, What a Way To Go—1964, Return from the Ashes—1965, Battle for the Planet of the Apes—1968, Conquest of the Planet of the Apes—1969, The Reincarnation of Peter Proud—1971, St. Ives—1973, The White Buffalo—1977, CaboBlanco—1981, Happy Birthday To Me—1981

TOBACK, James
  Agent: Jeff Berg, ICM
  8899 Beverly Boulevard
  Los Angeles, CA 90048
  Telephone: (213) 550-4000
credits: Fingers—1978, Exposed—1982

TOWNE, Robert
(see also Screenwriters)
  San Pedro Films, c/o Warner Bros.
  4000 Warner Blvd.
  Burbank, CA 91522
  Telephone: (213) 954-2037
credits: Personal Best—1982

TRIKONIS, Gus
  Agent: Herb Tobias & Assoc.
  1901 Ave. of the Stars, Suite 840
  Los Angeles, CA 90067
  Telephone: (213) 277-6211
credits: Touched By Love—1980, Take This Job and Shove It—1981

TRUMBULL, Douglas
  Business: Entertainment Effects Group
  13335 Maxella
  Venice, CA 90291
  Telephone: (213) 823-0433
credits: Silent Running—1971, Brainstorm—1982

TURMAN, Lawrence
(see also Producers)
  Bus.: The Turman-Foster Company
  Universal Studios
  100 Universal City Plaza
  Universal City, CA 91608
  Telephone: (213) 985-4321
credits: Marriage of a Stockbroker—1971, Second Thoughts—1982

VAN HORN, Buddy
  Agent: William Morris Agency
  151 El Camino Dr.
  Beverly Hills, CA 90212
  Telephone: (213) 274-7451
credits: Any Which Way You Can—1980

VERONA, Steve
(see also Screenwriters)
  Agent: William Morris Agency
  1350 Avenue of the Americas
  New York, NY 10010
  Telephone: (212) 586-5100
credits: The Lords of Flatbush—1974, Pipe Dreams—1976, Boardwalk—1979

WALTON, Frederick R.
  Agent: Robert Stein
  Paul Kohner, Inc.
  9169 Sunset Boulevard
  Los Angeles, CA 90069
  Telephone: (213) 550-1060

directors, motion picture

WALTON, Frederick, *continued*
credits: When A Stranger Calls—1981,
Aura—1982, Snowman—[upcoming]

WARD, David S.
(see also Screenwriters)
   Agent: ICM
   8899 Beverly Boulevard
   Los Angeles, CA 90048
   Telephone: (213) 550-4000
credits: Cannery Row—1981

WEILL, Claudia
   Business: Cyclops Films
   1969 Broadway, Room 1109
   New York, NY 10019
   Telephone: (212) 265-1375
credits: Girlfriends—1978, It's My
Turn—1980

WEIR, Peter
credits: Picnic At Hanging Rock—1975,
The Last Wave—1978, The Plumber—
1979, Gallipoli—1981, The Year of Living
Dangerously—1982

WENDERS, Wim
   Agent: Paul Kohner, Inc.
   9169 Sunset Boulevard
   Los Angeles, CA 90069
   Telephone: (213) 550-1060
credits: Alice in the Cities—1974, The
Wrong Move—1975, The American
Friend—Kings of the Road—1976, Ham-
m e t — 1 9 8 2

WENDKOS, Paul
   Agent: Creative Artists Agency, Inc.
   1888 Century Park East
   Los Angeles, CA 90067
   Telephone: (213) 277-4545
credits: Angel Baby—1960, Guns of the
Magnificent Seven—1967, Cannon for
Cordoba—1970, The Mephisto Waltz—
1971, Special Delivery—1976

WERNER, Peter
   Agent: Robert Stein
   Paul Kohner, Inc.
   9169 Sunset Boulevard
   Los Angeles, CA 90069
   (213) 550-1060
credits: Don't Cry, It's Only Thunder—
1982

WILDER, Billy
   Bus. Mgr.: Equitable Investment Corp.
   6253 Hollywood Boulevard, Suite 1122
   Hollywood, CA 90028
   Telephone: (213) 469-2975
credits: The Major and the Minor—1942,
The Lost Weekend—1945, Sunset Boule-
vard—1950, Stalag 17—1953, Sabrina—
1954, The Seven Year Itch—1955, The
Spirit of St. Louis—1957, Some Like It
Hot—1959, The Apartment—1960, One
Two Three—1961, Irma la Douce—1963,
Kiss Me Stupid—1964, The Fortune
Cookie—1966, The Private Life of Sher-
lock Holmes—1970, Avanti!—1972, The
Front Page—1974, Fedora—1978, Buddy
Buddy—1981

WINNER, Michael
   Business: 6-8 Sackville Street
   London W1X 1DD, England
   Telephone: 01-734-8385
credits: The Jokers—1967, Hannibal
Brooks—1968, The Games—1969, Law-
man—1970, The Nightcomers—1971,
Chato's Land—1971, The Mechanic—
1972, Scorpio—1972, The Stone Killer—
1973, Death Wish—1974, Won Ton Ton,
The Dog Who Saved Hollywood—1976,
The Sentinel—1977, The Big Sleep—
1978, Firepower—1979, Death Wish II—
1981

WISE, Robert
(see also Producers)
   Business: Robert Wise Productions

WISE, Robert, *continued*
Sunset Gower Studios
1438 North Gower, Suite 562
Hollywood, CA 90028
Telephone: (213) 461-3864
credits: Curse of the Cat People—1944, Mademoiselle Fifi—1944, Body Snatchers—1945, Born to Kill—1947, Blood on the Moon—1948, The Set-Up—1949, Three Secrets—1950, The Day the Earth Stood Still—1951, Captive City—1952, So Big—1952, Destination Gobi—1953, The Desert Rats—1953, Executive Suite—1954, Helen of Troy—1955, Tribute to a Bad Man—1956, Somebody Up There Likes Me—1956, This Could Be the Night—1957, Until They Sail—1957, Run Silent, Run Deep—1958, I Want To Live—1958, Odds Against Tomorrow—1959, Two For the Seesaw—1962, The Haunting—1963, The Sound of Music—1965, The Sand Pebbles—1966, Westside Story—1966, Star!—1968, The Andromeda Strain—1971, Two People—1972, The Hindenburg—1975, Audrey Rose—1976, Star Trek–The Motion Picture—1979

YATES, Peter
Agent: Chasin-Park-Citron Agency
9255 Sunset Blvd.
Los Angeles, CA
Telephone (213) 273-7190
credits: Summer Holiday—1962, One Way Pendulum—1964, Robbery—1967, Bullitt—1968, John and Mary—1969, Murphy's War—1971, The Hot Rock—1972, The Friends of Eddie Coyle—1973, For Pete's Sake—1974, Mother, Jugs and Speed—1976, The Deep—1977, Breaking Away—1979, Eyewitness—1981, Krull—1982

YORKIN, Bud
Tandem Productions
1901 Avenue of the Stars
Los Angeles, CA 90067
Telephone: (213) 553-3600

credits: Come Blow Your Horn—1963, Never Too Late—1965, Divorce, American Style—1967, Inspector Clouseau—1968, Start the Revolution Without Me—1970, The Thief Who Came to Dinner—1973

YOUNG, Robert M.
Agent: ICM
40 West 57th St.
New York, NY 10019
Telephone: (212) 556-5600
credits: Short Eyes—1977, Alambrista—1978, Rich Kids—1979, One Trick Pony—1980

YOUNG, Terence
Agent: Kurt Frings
Telephone: (213) 274-8881
credits: Dr. No—1962, From Russia With Love—1963, Thunderball—1965, The Poppy is Also a Flower—1966, Wait Until Dark—1967, You Only Live Twice—1967, Mayerling—1968, The Christmas Tree—1969, Grand Slam—1970, Cold Sweat—1970, Red Sun—1971, The Valachi Papers—1972, War Goddess—1973, The Klansman—1974, Inchon—1981

ZEFFIRELLI, Franco
credits: Romeo and Juliet—1967, The Taming of the Shrew—1967, Champ—1979, Endless Love—1981

ZEMECKIS, Robert
Agent: Jeff Berg, ICM
8899 Beverly Blvd.
Los Angeles, CA 90048
Telephone: (213) 550-4000
credits: I Wanna Hold Your Hand—1978, Used Cars—1980

directors, motion picture

ZIEFF, Howard
  20th Century-Fox
  10201 West Pico Blvd.
  Los Angeles, CA 90035
  Telephone: (213) 203-2941

credits: Slither—1972, Hearts of the West—1975, House Calls—1978, The Main Event—1979, Private Benjamin—1980

ZINNEMAN, Fred
  Agent: Stan Kamen
  William Morris Agency
  Beverly Hills, CA 90212
  Telephone: (213) 274-7451

credits: The Seventh Cross—1943, The Search—1947, The Men—1949, High Noon—1951, Member of the Wedding—1952, From Here to Eternity—1953, Oklahoma!—1955, A Hatful of Rain—1956, The Nun's Story—1958, The Sundowners—1960, Behold a Pale Horse—1964, A Man for All Seasons—1966, The Day of the Jackal—1973, Julia—1977, Five Days In Summer—1982

ZUCKER, David, and ZUCKER, Jerry
  11777 San Vicente Blvd.
  Los Angeles, CA 90049
  Telephone: (213) 820-1942

credits: Airplane—1980 *(with Jim Abrahams)*

PRODUCERS

ADLER, Allen
Business: The IndieProd Co.
10201 W. Pico Boulevard
Los Angeles, CA 90035
Telephone: (213) 277-3246

credits: Making Love (co-produced with Dan Melnick)—1982

ALDRICH, William
Office: The Aldrich Co.
606 North Larchmont
Los Angeles, CA 90004
Telephone: (213) 462-6511

credits: All The Marbles—1981

ALLEN, Irwin
Business: Irwin Allen Productions
Columbia Pictures
Columbia Plaza
Burbank, CA 91505
Telephone: (213) 954-3601

credits: The Sea Around Us—1953, The Big Circus—1959, Voyage to the Bottom of the Sea—1961, The Wrecking Crew—1968, The Poseidon Adventure—1972, The Towering Inferno—1974, The Swarm—1978, Beyond the Poseidon Adventure—1979, When Time Ran Out—1980

ALLYN, William
2385 Castilian Drive
Los Angeles, CA 90068
(213) 851-1830

credits: Rich and Famous—1981

ALTMAN, Robert B.
(See also Directors)
Business: Landscape Films
12115 Magnolia Blvd., Suite 123
North Hollywood, CA
91607   Telephone: (213) 509-0259

credits: Welcome to L.A.—1977, The Late Show—1977, Remember My Name—1978, Rich Kids—1979

ARKOFF, Samuel Z.
Business: Arkoff International Pictures
9200 Sunset Blvd., Penthouse 3
Los Angeles, CA 90069
Telephone: (213) 278-7600

recent credits (producer of over 500 films): Dressed to Kill—1980, The Amityville Horror—1981, The Serpent—1982

ASSEYEV, Tamara and
ROSE, Alex
Office: MGM Studios
10202 W. Washington Boulevard
Culver City, CA 90230
Telephone: (213) 558-6470

credits: Drive In—1977, Big Wednesday (as Exec. Producers))—1978, I Wanna Hold Your Hand—1978, Norma Rae—1979

AVEDIS, Howard
(see also Screenwriters)
Business: Hickmar Productions
4000 Warner Boulevard
Burbank, CA 91522
Telephone: (213) 954-6000

credits: Separate Ways—1981, The Fifth Floor—1979

AVNET, Jon and
TISCH, Steve
(see also Producers, Movies for TV)
Business: Tisch/Avnet Productions, Inc.
515 North Robertson Boulevard
Los Angeles, CA 90048
Telephone: (213) 278-7680

credits: Coast to Coast—1980

AZOFF, Irving
Business: 9044 Melrose Avenue
Los Angeles, CA 90069
Telephone: (213) 859-1900

credits: Urban Cowboy—1980, Fast Times—1982

BARISH, Keith
Business: Keith Barish Productions
8380 Melrose Avenue
Los Angeles, CA 90069
Telephone: (213) 852-7006

credits: Endless Love *(as executive producer)*—1981, Sophie's Choice *(co-produced with Alan J. Pakula)*—1983

**BART, Peter and
PALEVSKY, Max**

credits: Fun with Dick and Jane—1977, Islands in the Stream—1977

BEATTY, Warren
(see also Directors)
Business: Paramount Studios
Los Angeles, CA 90038
Telephone: (213) 468-5000

credits: Bonnie and Clyde—1967, Shampoo—1975, Heaven Can Wait—1978, Reds—1981

BECKERMAN, Sidney
Business: Beckerman Productions
3968 Overland Avenue, Suite 211
Culver City, CA 90230
Telephone: (213) 558-5453

credits: Kelly's Heroes—1970, Joe Kidd—1972, Marathon Man—1976, Bloodline—1979, Serial—1980, A Stranger is Watching—1982, Aura—1982

BILL, Tony
(See also Directors)
Business: 73 Market Street
Venice, CA 90291
Telephone: (213) 396-5937

credits: Deadhead Miles—1970, Steelyard Blues—1972, The Sting—1973, Hearts of the West—1975, Harry and Walter Go to New York—1976, Boulevard Nights—1979, Going in Style—1979

BLATT, Daniel
Business: Blatt-Singer Productions
4000 Warner Boulevard
Burbank, CA 91522
Telephone: (213) 954-6000

credits: The Howling—1981

BRADEN, William
Business: Dunatai Corporation
P.O. Box 714
Van Nuys, CA 91408

credits: Headgames—1978, Running Scared—1979

BRAUNSBERG, Andrew
credits: Being There—1979

BREGMAN, Martin
Business: Martin Bregman Prod.
614 Lexington Avenue
New York, NY 10022
100 Universal City Plaza
Universal City, CA 91608
Telephone: (213) 508-2813

credits: Serpico—1973, Dog Day Afternoon—1975, *(with Martin Elfand)*—1975, The Next Man—1976, The Seduction of Joe Tynan—1979, Simon—1980, The Four Seasons—1981, Venom—1982, Eddie Macon's Run—1983

BROCCOLI, Albert R.
Office: MGM Studios
164 Thalberg Bldg.
10202 West Washington Blvd.
Culver City, CA 90230
Telephone: (213) 558-6570

credits: Red Beret—1952, Hell Below Zero—1953, Black Knight—1954, Prize of Gold—1955, Cockleshell Heroes—1956, Safari—1956, April in Portugal—1956, Fire Down Below,—1956, Odongo—1956, Pickup Alley—1957, Arrivederci Roma—1957, Interpol—1957, How to Murder a Rich Uncle—1957, High Flight—1958, No Time to Die—1958, The

BROCCOLI, Albert R., *continued*

Man Inside—1958, Killers of Kilimanjaro—1958, Bandit of Zhobe—1958, In the Nick—1959, Jazz Boat—1960, Let's Get Married—1960, The Trials of Oscar Wilde—1960, Idol on Parade—1960, Johnny Nobody—1961, Call Me Bwana—1963, Chitty Chitty Bang Bang—1967; *James Bond Films:* Dr. No—1962, From Russia with Love—1963, Goldfinger—1964, Thunderball—1965, You Only Live Twice—1967, On Her Majesty's Secret Service—1969, Diamonds Are Forever—1971, Live and Let Die—1972, The Man with the Golden Gun—1974, The Spy Who Loved Me—1977, Moonraker—1979, For Your Eyes Only—1981; *Recipient: Irving Thalberg Memorial Award—1981*

BROOKS, Mel
(see also Directors, Screenwriters)
　Business: Brooksfilms, Ltd.
　P.O. Box 900
　Beverly Hills, CA 90213
　Telephone: (213) 203-1375
credits: High Anxiety—1977, The History of the World–Part I—1981

BROWN, David and
ZANUCK, Richard
　Business: Zanuck/Brown Co.
　P.O. Box 900
　Beverly Hills, CA 90213
　Telephone: (213) 203-3183

credits: The Sting—1973, The Sugarland Express—1974, Jaws—1977, MacArthur—1977, Jaws II—1978, The Island—1980, Neighbors—1981, The Verdict—1982

BROWN, Howard
　Business: C & C Brown Productions
　4000 Warner Boulevard
　Burbank, CA 91522
　Telephone: (213) 954-6000

credits: Cheech and Chong's Next Movie—1980, Cheech and Chong's Nice Dreams—1981, Things Are Tough All Over—1982

BRUCKHEIMER, Jerry
　Office: Universal Studios
　100 Universal Plaza
　Universal City, CA 91608
　Telephone: (213) 985-4321

credits: Farewell My Lovely *(with George Pappas)*—1975, March or Die *(with Dick Richards)*—1977, Defiance *(with William S. Gilmore, Jr.)*—1980, American Gigolo—1980, Thief *(with Ronnie Caan)*—1981, Cat People—1982, Young Doctors in Love—1982

CAPRA, Frank, Jr.
　Office: Embassy Pictures
　956 Seward Street
　Los Angeles, CA 90038

credits: Trapped Beneath the Sea-197?, Born Again—1978, The Black Marble—1980, An Eye For An Eye—1981, Vice Squad *(as executive producer with Sandy Howard and Robert Rehme)*—1982

CARR, Allan
　Business: 1220 Benedict Canyon Drive
　Beverly Hills, CA 90210
　Telephone: (213) 274-2490

credits: Grease—1978, Can't Stop the Music—1980, Grease 2 *(with Robert Stigwood)*—1982, Where The Boys Are—[upcoming]

CARELLI, Joann
　Business: Partisan Productions
　9336 West Washington Boulevard
　Culver City, CA 90230
　Telephone: (213) 204-4020

credits: The Deer Hunter *(as assoc. prod.)*—1978, Heaven's Gate—1980

CARROLL, Gordon
Contact: Rastar Films, Inc.
300 Colgems Square
Burbank, CA 91505
Telephone: (213) 954-2748

credits: How to Murder Your Wife—1963, Luv—1967, Cool Hand Luke—1967, The April Fools—1969, Pat Garrett and Billy the Kid—1973, Alien—1979, Blue Thunder—1982

CHAPIN, Douglas and
KROST, Barry
Business: The Movie Company
336 North Foothill Road
Beverly Hills, CA 90210
Telephone: (213) 271-7254

credits: Love at First Bite—1978, Thursday The 12th—1981

CHARTOFF, Robert and
WINKLER, Irwin
Business: Chartoff-Winkler
Productions, Inc.
10125 W. Washington Blvd.
Culver City, CA 90230
Telephone: (213) 204-0474

credits: The Split—1968, Leo the Last—1969, They Shoot Horses, Don't They?—1969, The Strawberry Statement—1970, The Gang that Couldn't Shoot Straight—1971, The New Centurions—1972, Up the Sandbox—1972, The Mechanic—1972, S*P*Y*S—1974, Peeper—1975, The Gambler—1975, Rocky—1976, Nickelodeon—1976, New York, New York—1977, Sons—1978, Comes A Horseman—1978, Rocky II—1979, Raging Bull—1980, Rocky III—1982, The Right Stuff—1983

COBLENZ, Walter
Business: Bellisle Productions
11950 Ventura Blvd.
Studio City, CA 91604
Telephone: (213) 508-0306

credits: The Candidate—1970, All The President's Men—1976, The Onion Field—1979, The Legend of the Lone Ranger—1981

COHEN, Herman
Business: Cobra Media, Inc.—
Cohen Productions
650 North Bronson Avenue
Los Angeles, CA 90004
Telephone: (213) 466-3111

credits: I Was a Teenage Werewolf, I Was a Teenage Frankenstein, Craze—1975, Tomorrow We Die—1976, The Strangers Gundown—1977, The Dragon Lives—1979

COPPOLA, Francis
(see also Directors)
Business: Zoetrope Studios
1040 North Las Palmas
Hollywood, CA 90038
Telephone: (213) 463-7191

credits: THX 1138—1970, American Graffiti—1973, The Conversation—1974, The Black Stallion—1979, Apocalypse Now—1979, The Outsiders (executive producer)—1982

CORMAN, Roger
Business: New World Pictures, Inc.
11600 San Vicente
Los Angeles, CA 90049
Telephone: (213) 820-6733

credits: Bloody Mama—1970, Gas—1970, Von Richtofen and Brown—1971, Boxcar Bertha—1972, I Escaped from Devils Island—1973, Cockfighter—1974, Death Race 2000—1975, Fighting Mad—1976, Moving Violation—1976, Thunder and Lightning—1976, Hollywood Boulevard—1976, Jackson County Jail—1976, Eat My Dust—1976, Texas Dynamite Chase—1976, Cannonball—1976, Grand Theft Auto—1977, I Never Promised You A Rose Garden—1977, Deathsport—

producers, motion picture

CORMAN, Roger, *continued*

1978, Blackout—1978, The Bees—1978, Avalanche—1978, Piranha—1978, Rock N' Roll High School—1979, Up From the Depth—1979, Saint Jack—1979, Touch Me and Die—1979, Humanoids From the Deep—1980, Smokey Bites the Dust—1980, Battle Beyond the Stars—1980, Outside Chance—1980, Follow That Car—1980, Nightfall—1980, Firecracker—1980, Mindwarp: An Infinity of Terror—1981, Saturday the 14th—1981

CRAWFORD, Robert
Business: Pan-Arts Productions
4000 Warner Boulevard
Burbank, CA 91522
Telephone: (213) 954-6000

credits: A Little Romance *(with Yves Rousset-Rouard)*—1979, The World According to Garp *(with George Roy Hill)*—1982

CURTIS, Bruce Cohn
Business: Compass International Films
9229 West Sunset Boulevard
Los Angeles, CA 90069
Telephone: (213) 273-9125

credits: Roller Boogie—1979, Hell Night—1981, The Seduction *(with Irwin Yablans)*—1982

DAVID, Pierre
Business: Mutual Productions
Montreal, Canada

credits: Videodrome—1982

DAVIS, Peter and
PANZER, William
Business: Davis-Panzer Productions
Sunset-Gower Studios
1438 North Gower Street
Hollywood, CA 90028
Telephone: (213) 463-2343

credits: The Death Collector *(as executive producer)*—1977, Stunts *(as executive producer)*—1978, Steel—1979, St. Helens *(co-produced with William Panzer)*—1981, O'Hara's Wife *(with William Panzer)*—1982, The Jupiter Menace *(as executive producer)*—1982, The Osterman Weekend *(co-produced with William Panzer)*—1983

DAVISON, Jon
Office: Paramount Pictures
5555 Melrose
Los Angeles, CA 90038
Telephone: (213) 468-5000

credits: Hollywood Boulevard—1976, Grand Theft Auto—1977, Piranha—1978, Airplane!—1980, White Dog—1981

DEELEY, Michael
Office: Tandem Productions
1901 Avenue of the Stars, Suite 1600
Los Angeles, CA 90067
Telephone: (213) 557-2323

credits: The Deer Hunter—1979, Blade Runner—1982

DE LAURENTIIS, Dino
Business: Dino De Laurentiis Corp.
1 Gulf & Western Plaza
New York, NY 10023
Telephone: (212) 550-8700

credits: Barbarella—1968, Waterloo—1970, The Valachi Papers—1972, The Stone Killer—1973, Serpico—1973, Death Wish—1974, Mandingo—1975, Three Days of the Condor—1975, Lipstick—1976, The Shootist—1976, King Kong—1976, The Serpent's Egg—1977, King of the Gypsies—1979, The Hurricane—1979, Flash Gordon—1980, Halloween II—1981, Ragtime—1981, Conan the Barbarian—1982

DEUTSCH, Stephen
Business: Summerland Productions
20th Century-Fox Studios
10201 West Pico Boulevard
Los Angeles, CA 90035
Telephone: (213) 277-2211
credits: Somewhere in Time—1980

DE WAAY, Larry
Business: 601 North Bronson Avenue
Hollywood, CA 90004
Telephone: (213) 469-6097
credits: The Dogs of War—1981, Yentl *(as executive producer)*—[not yet released]

DOUGLAS, Michael
Office: Big Stick Productions
4000 Warner Boulevard
Burbank, CA 91522
Telephone: (213) 954-3416
credits: One Flew Over the Cuckoo's Nest—1975, The China Syndrome—1979

DRABINSKY, Garth and
MICHAELS, Joel B.
Business: Tiberius Productions
Toronto International Studios
Toronto, Canada
credits: Tribute—1980

EDELMAN, Kate and
UBAUD, Jean
Business: Edelman-Ubaud Productions
9901 Durant Drive, Suite H
Beverly Hills, CA 90212
Telephone: (213) 557-1917
credits: TAG: The Assassination Game—1981, High Jinx—[upcoming]

EDWARDS, Blake
(see also Directors)
Business: Trellis Enterprises
1888 Century Park East, Suite 1616
Los Angeles, CA 90067
Telephone: (213) 553-6741
Studio Office: MGM
Telephone: (213) 836-3000, Ext. 6300

EDWARDS, Blake
credits: Days of Wine and Roses—1962, The Tamarind Seed—1976, The Return of the Pink Panther—1974, The Pink Panther Strikes Again—1976, The Revenge of the Pink Panther—1978, ''10''—1979, S.O.B.—1981, Victor, Victoria—1982

ELFAND, Martin
Office: Paramount Pictures
5555 Melrose Ave.
Los Angeles, CA 90038
Telephone: (213) 858-6090
credits: Dog Day Afternoon*(co-produced with Martin Bregman)*—1975, It's My Turn—1980, An Officer and a Gentleman—1981

EVANS, Robert
Bus. Office: Paramount Pictures, Inc.
5555 Melrose Avenue
Los Angeles, CA 90038
Telephone: (213) 468-5000, Ext. 1954
credits: Love Story—1970, The Great Gatsby—1974, Chinatown—1974, Marathon Man—1976, Black Sunday—1977, Players—1978, Urban Cowboy—1980, Popeye—1980
[Has a producing relationship with Paramount]

FANCHER, Hampton
(see also Screenwriters)
Bus. Manager: Hersh Panitch & Co.
21243 Ventura Boulevard, Suite 201
Woodland Hills, CA 91364
Telephone: (213) 999-2530
Attorney: Ken Suddleson
Telephone: (213) 552-7700
credits: Blade Runner *(as executive producer)*—1982, Salvation—[upcoming]

FEITSHANS, Buzz
credits: Hardcore—1979, Conan—1982, First Blood—[not yet released]

producers, motion picture

FELDMAN, Edward S.
Office: 10201 West Pico Boulevard
Los Angeles, CA 90004
Telephone: (213) 277-2211

credits: Save the Tiger—1973, The Other Side of the Mountain—1975

FIELDS, Freddie
Office: MGM Studios
10202 W. Washington Blvd.
Culver City, CA 90230
Telephone: (213) 558-5411

credits: Lipstick—1976, Looking for Mr. Goodbar—1977, Citizens Band—1977, American Gigolo—1979, Wholly Moses!—1980, Victory—1981, Escape to Victory—1982

FOLSEY, George, Jr.

credits: An American Werewolf in London—1981

FOREMAN, John
Business: J. F. Productions
MGM Studios
10202 West Washington Blvd.
Culver City, CA 90230
Telephone: (213) 558-5030

credits: Winning—1969, Butch Cassidy and the Sundance Kid—1969, Puzzle of a Downfall Child—1970, W.U.S.A.—1970, They Might Be Giants—1971, The Life and Times of Judge Roy Bean—1972, The Effect of Gamma Rays on Man-in-the-Moon Marigolds—1972, Pocket Money—1973, Sometimes A Great Notion—1973, MacIntosh Man—1974, The Man Who Would Be King—1976, Bobby Deerfield—1977, The Great Train Robbery—1979, Brainstorm—1982, Eureka—[upcoming]

FOSTER, David
Business: Turman-Foster Co.
Office: Twentieth Century-Fox
10201 W. Pico Blvd.
Los Angeles, CA 90064
Telephone: (213) 203-3156

credits: McCabe and Mrs. Miller—1972, The Getaway—1973; *(co-produced with Lawrence Turman):* Heroes—1977, Tribute—1980, Caveman—1981, The Thing—1982, Second Thoughts—1982

FRANK, Melvin
Agent: William Morris Agency
151 El Camino Drive
Beverly Hills, CA 90212
Telephone: (213) 274-7451

credits: A Touch of Class—1973, The Prisoner of Second Avenue—1975, The Duchess and the Dirtwater Fox—1976, Lost and Found—1979, Not a Penny Less—[upcoming]

FRANKOVICH, Mike
Business: 9200 Sunset Boulevard
Suite 920
Los Angeles, CA 90069
Telephone: (213) 278-0920

credits: Marooned—1969, Bob & Carol & Ted & Alice—1969, Cactus Flower—1969, Doctor's Wives—1970, $—1971, Butterflies Are Free—1972, Forty Carats—1973, Report to the Commissioner—1974, The Shootist—1976

FREDERICKSON, Gray and ROOS, Fred
Office: Zoetrope Studios
1040 North Las Palmas
Los Angeles, CA 90038
Telephone: (213) 463-7191

credits: Apocalypse Now—1979, Hammet—1982, One from the Heart—1982, The Outsiders—[not yet released]

FRIEDMAN, Stephen
Business: Kings Road Productions
The Burbank Studios
4000 Warner Boulevard
Burbank, CA 91522
Telephone: (213) 954-6602

FRIEDMAN, Stephen, *continued*
credits: The Last Picture Show—1970, Lovin' Molly—1974, Slapshot—1977, Blood Brothers—1978, Fastbreak—1978, Little Darlings—1979, Hero At Large—1980, Eye of the Needle—1981, Incubus—1982

GILBERT, Bruce
Office: IPC Films
10201 West Pico Blvd.
Los Angeles, CA 90035
Telephone: (213) 203-2605
credits: Coming Home *(as associate producer)*—1978, China Syndrome *(as executive producer)*—1979, Nine to Five—1980, Rollover—1981, On Golden Pond—1981

GILMORE, William S.
credits: Tough Dreams—1981

GOLAN, Menahem, and GLOBUS, Yoram
Business: Cannon Films
6464 Sunset Boulevard, Suite 1150
Hollywood, CA 90028
Telephone: (213) 469-8124
credits: Body and Soul—1981, X-Ray—1981, Lady Chatterley's Lover—1981, Enter the Ninja—1981, Death Wish II *(as executive producers)*—1982, Revenge of the Ninja—[not yet released]

GOLDBERG, Leonard
Business: Mandy Films, MGM Studios
10202 West Washington Blvd.
Culver City, CA 90230
Telephone: (213) 558-6387
credits: All Night Long *(co-produced with Jerry Weintraub)*—1981, War Games—1982

GORDON, Lawrence
Office: Paramount Pictures
5555 Melrose Avenue
Los Angeles, CA 90038
Telephone: (213) 468-5000
credits: Hard Times—1975, Rolling Thunder—1977, The End—1978, The Driver—1978, Hooper—1978, The Warriors—1979, Paternity—1981, Jekyll and Hyde … Together Again—1982

GOTTFRIED, Howard
credits: The Hospital—1971, Network—1976, Altered States—1979

GREENHUT, Robert
Business: M.O.S. Services, Inc.
150 East 58th Street
New York, NY 10022
Telephone: (212) 688-5333
credits: Annie Hall *(as executive producer)*—1977, Interiors *(as executive producer)*—1978, Manhattan *(as executive producer)*—1979, Stardust Memories—1980, Arthur—1981

GREISMAN, Alan
Business: Three Wheel Productions
Twentieth Century-Fox Studios
10201 West Pico Boulevard
Los Angeles, CA 90035
Telephone: (213) 277-2211
credits: Modern Problems—1981

GRUSKOFF, Michael
Office: Grusskoff Film Organization
10201 W. Pico Boulevard
Los Angeles, CA 90064
Telephone: (213) 277-2211
credits: Silent Running—1971, Young Frankenstein—1974, Rafferty and the Gold Dust Twins—1975, Lucky Lady—1975, Quest For Fire *(as executive producer*—1982, My Favorite Year—1982

GUBER, Peter

credits (all as co-executive producer with Jon Peters): An American Werewolf in London—1981, Missing—1982

HARRISON, George

Business: Handmade Films
26 Cadogan Square
London S.W. 1, England
Telephone: 01-581-1265

credits (all as executive producer with Denis O'Brien): Life of Brian—1979, Time Bandits—1981, Scrubbers—1982

HAWN, Goldie

Agent: William Morris Agency
151 El Camino Drive
Beverly Hills, CA 90212
Telephone: (213) 274-7451

credits: Pvt. Benjamin—1980, Chicago (with Martin Richards)—[upcoming], Protocol—[upcoming]

HELLER, Paul

Business: 1666 N. Beverly Drive
Beverly Hills, CA 90210
Telephone: (213) 275-4477

credits: David and Lisa—1962, The Eavesdropper—1966, Secret Ceremony—1968, Enter the Dragon—1973, Choice of Weapons—1976, Outlaw Blues—1977, The Pack—1978, The Promise—1979, First Monday in October (with Martha Scott)—1981

HELLMAN, Jerome

Bus.: Jerome Hellman Productions
68 Malibu Colony Drive
Malibu, CA 90265
Telephone: (213) 456-3361

credits: The World of Henry Orient—1964, A Fine Madness—1966, Midnight Cowboy—1969, The Day of the Locust—1975, Coming Home—1978, Promises in the Dark—1979, Klondike

HILL, Debra

Business: Pumpkin Pie Productions
3110 Burbank Blvd.
Burbank, CA 91505
Telephone: (213) 845-8511

credits: Halloween—1978, The Fog—1980, Escape From New York—1981, Halloween II (co-produced with John Carpenter)—1981, Halloween III—1982, Season of the Witch—1982

HITZIG, Rupert and
KING, Alan

credits: Electa-Glide in Blue—1971, Cattle Annie and Little Britches—1981, Wolfen—1981, Happy Birthday Gemini—19__

HOWARD, Sandy

Business: Sandy Howard Productions
8755 Shoreham Drive, Suite 201
Los Angeles, CA 90069
Telephone: (213) 657-8300

credits: The Neptune Factor, The Devil's Rain, Skyriders, Man in the Wilderness, A Man Called Horse—1970, The Return of a Man Called Horse—1972, Echoes of Summer, Embryo, The Island of Dr. Moreau—1976, Crunch, Deathship, Circle of Iron, City on Fire, Meteor—1979, Savage Harvest—1981, Vice Squad—1982

IMMERMAN, William J.

Business: Cinema Group, Inc.
8758 Venice Blvd.
Los Angeles, CA 90034
Telephone: (213) 204-0102

credits: Take This Job and Shove It—1980, Southern Comfort—1981, Hysterical—1982

JAFFE, Herb

Business: Camp Hill Productions
3910 Overland Avenue
Culver City, CA 90230
Telephone: (213) 559-8632

credits: The Wind and the Lion—1975,

JAFFE, Herb, *continued*
Demon Seed—197__, Time After Time—1978, Who'll Stop the Rain—197__, Those Lips, Those Eyes—197__, Motel Hell—1980, It's All in the Game—1982, Lords of Discipline—1982

JAFFE, Stanley
Office: Stanley Jaffe Productions
660 Madison Avenue
New York, NY 10021
Telephone: (213) 421-4410
credits: Goodbye Columbus—1969, A New Leaf—1971, Bad Company—1972, Man on a Swing—1973, The Bad News Bears—1976, Kramer vs. Kramer—1979, Taps—1981, Without A Trace—1983

JEWISON, Norman
(See also Directors)
Business: Timberlane Productions
9336 West Washington Blvd.
Culver City, CA 90230
Telephone: (213) 836-5537
Agent: William Morris Agency
151 El Camino Drive
Beverly Hills, CA 90212
Telephone: (213) 274-7451
credits: The Landlord—1970, Jesus Christ, Superstar *(co-produced with Robert Stigwood)*—1973, Billy Two Hats—1975, The Dogs of War *(exec. prod. with Patrick Palmer)*—1981, Best Friends *(co-produced with Patrick Palmer)*—1982

JOFFE, Charles H. and ROLLINS, Jack
Business: Rollins/Joffe/Morra/
Brezner, Inc.
130 West 57th Street
New York, NY 10019
Telephone: (212) 582-1940
L.A. Office: Paramount Pictures
5555 Melrose Avenue
Los Angeles, CA 90038
Telephone: (213) 468-5000

credits: Take the Money and Run—1969, Bananas—1971, Everything You Always Wanted to Know About Sex—1972, Sleeper—1973, Love and Death—1975, The Front—1976, Annie Hall—1977, Interiors—1978, Manhattan—1979, Stardust Memories—1980, Arthur *(as exec. prod.)*—1981, A Midsummer Night's Sex Comedy *(as Executive Producer)*

JOHNSON, Mary Lea and RICHARDS, Martin
Business: Producer Circle Co.
9200 Sunset Boulevard, Suite 920
Los Angeles, CA 90069
Telephone: (213) 278-1422
credits: Fort Apache: The Bronx—1981, Coyote—[upcoming], Chicago *(with Goldie Hawn)*—[upcoming]

KASTNER, Elliott
Office: Universal City Studios
Building 84
Universal City, CA 91608
Telephone: (213) 508-2071
credits: Bus Rileys Back In Town—1965, Harper—1966, The Night of the Following Day—1968, Where Eagles Dare—1969, The Walking Stick—1969, A Severed Head—1970, Villain—1971, When Eight Bells Toll—1971, The Night Comers—1971, Zee and Co.—1972, Fear is the Key—1972, The Long Goodbye—1973, Cops and Robbers—1973, Harrowhouse 11—1974, Rancho De Luxe—1974, Love and Death—1975, Farewell My Lovely—1975, Russian Roulette—1975, Swashbuckler—1976, The Missouri Breaks *(as co-producer)*—1976, 92 in the Shade—1976, The Big Sleep—1978, ffolkes—1979, Golden Girl *(as executive producer)*—1979, The First Deadly Sin—1980, Death Valley—1982

producers, motion picture

KATZKA, Gabriel
Business: Pantheon Pictures
10201 West Pico Blvd.
Los Angeles, CA 90064
Telephone: (213) 277-2211
credits: The Beast Within—1978, The Falcon and the Snowman—[upcoming]

KAZANJIAN, Howard G.
Business: Lucasfilm, Ltd.
P. O. Box 2009
San Rafael, CA 94912
Telephone: (415) 457-5282
credits: More American Graffiti—1979, Raiders of the Lost Ark *(executive producer with George Lucas)*—1981, Revenge of the Jedi—1983

KAYE, Nora
Business: MGM Studios
10202 West Washington Blvd.
Culver City, CA 90230
Telephone: (213) 836-3000
credits: Pennies from Heaven *(co-producer with Herbert Ross)*

KELLER, Max and Micheline
Business: Inter Planetary Productions
14225 Ventura Blvd.
Sherman Oaks, CA 91423
Telephone: (213) 981-4950
credits: Deadly Blessing—1981

KING, Alan and
HITZIG, Rupert
Business: King-Hitzig Productions
credits: Cattle Annie and Little Britches—1981, Wolfen—1981

KIRKWOOD, Gene
Business: Koch-Kirkwood
　　　　Entertainment
Twentieth-Century Fox
10201 West Pico Blvd.
Los Angeles, CA 90035
Telephone: (213) 203-3532

credits: Rocky—1976, New York, New York—1977, Comes A Horseman—1979, The Idolmaker—1980, The Pope of Greenwich Village—[upcoming]

KOCH, Howard W.
Office: Paramount Pictures
5555 Melrose Avenue
Los Angeles, CA 90038
Telephone: (213) 468-5000, Ext. 2333
credits—(as executive producer): X-15—1961, Sergeants Three—1962, The Manchurian Candidate—1962, Come Blow Your Horn—1963, Robin and the Seven Hood—1964, None But the Brave—1964, For Those Who Think Young—1964, The President's Analyst—1966, Dragonslayer—1981; *(as producer):* The Odd Couple—1967, A New Leaf—1969, On A Clear Day You Can See Forever—1970, Plaza Suite—1971, Star Spangled Girl, Last of the Red Hot Lovers—Jacqueline Susann's Once Is Not Enough—1977, Airplane!—1980, Some Kind of Hero—1982

KOCH, Howard W., Jr.
Business: Koch-Kirkwood
　　　　Entertainment
Twentieth-Century Fox
10201 West Pico Blvd.
Los Angeles, CA 90035
Telephone: (213) 203-3532

credits:—(as associate producer): Once Is Not Enough—1977, The Drowning Pool—1977; *(as executive producer):* The Other Side of Midnight—1977, Heaven Can Wait—1978, The Frisco Kid—1979; *(as producer):* Honky Tonk Freeway *(co-produced with Don Boyd)*—1980, The Idolmaker *(co-produced with Gene Kirkwood)*—1980

KONIGSBERG, Frank
(see also Producers—TV Films)
Business: 10201 West Pico Blvd.
Los Angeles, CA 90064
Telephone: (213) 203-3144

KONIGSBERG, Frank, *continued*

credits: Nine and a Half Weeks—[upcoming]

KRAMER, Stanley E.
(see also Directors)
Business: Stanley Kramer
Productions, Limited
P.O. Box 158
Bellvue, Washington 98009
Telephone: (206) 454-1785

credits: So This Is New York—1948, Champion—1949, Home of the Brave—1949, The Men—1950, Cyrano De Bergerac—1950, Death of a Salesman—1951, My Six Convicts—1952, The Sniper—1952, High Noon—1952, The Happy Time—1952, The Four Poster—1952, Eight Iron Men—1952, The Member of the Wedding—1952, The Juggler—1953, The 5,000 Fingers of Dr. T.—1953, The Wild One—1954, The Caine Mutiny—1954, Pressure Point—1962, A Child Is Waiting—1963, Invitation to a Gunfighter—1964, The Runner Stumbles—1979

**KROST, Barry and
CHAPIN, Douglas**
Business: The Movie Company
336 North Foothill Road
Beverly Hills, CA 90210
Telephone: (213) 271-7254

credits: Love at First Bite—1978, Thursday The 12th

KURTZ, Gary
Business: Kinetographics
P.O. Box 387
San Rafael, CA 94915
Telephone: (415) 459-2727

credits: American Graffiti—1973, Star Wars—1977, The Empire Strikes Back—1980

LADD, Alan, Jr.
Business: The Ladd Company
4000 Warner Boulevard
Burbank, CA 91522
Telephone: (213) 954-4400

credits: The Night Comes—1971, Fear Is the Key—1972

(President of the Ladd Co.)

LANDAU, Ely and Edie
Business: 2029 Century Park East, Suite 460
Los Angeles, CA 90067
Telephone: (213) 553-5010

credits: Long Day's Journey Into Night—1973, The Pawn Broker—1965, The Man in the Glass Booth—1965, Madwoman of Chaillot—1969, The Iceman Cometh—1973, A Delicate Balance—1973, The Three Sisters—1974, Rhinoceros—1974, In Celebration—1975, The Greek Tycoon—1978, Hopscotch—1980, Beatlemania—1981, The Chosen—1981

LANDERS, Hal
Business: The Hal Landers Co.
9255 Sunset Boulevard, Suite 915
Los Angeles, CA 90069
Telephone: (213) 550-8819

credits: The Gypsy Moths—1969, Monte Walsh—1970, The Hot Rock—1972, Death Wish—1974, Bank Shot—1974, Damnation Alley—1977, Joyride—1977, Death Wish II—1982

LANG, Jennings
Office: Universal Studios
100 Universal Plaza
Universal City, CA 91608
Telephone: (213) 508-2667

credits—(as executive producer): Coogan's Bluff—1968, Winning—1969, Act of the Heart—1970, Puzzle of a Downfall Child—1970, Tell Them Willie Boy is Here—1970, The Beguiled—1971,

producers, motion picture

LANG, Jennings, *continued*

They Might Be Giants—1971, Play Misty For Me—1971, Joe Kidd—1972, Pete n Tillie—1972, Slaughterhouse Five—1972, The Great Northfield Minnesota Raid— Breezy—1973, Charley Varrick—1973, High Plains Drifter—1973, Airport '75— 1974, Earthquake—1974, The Front Page—1974, The Great Waldo Pepper—1975, The Eiger Sanction—1975; *(as producer):* Swashbuckler—1976,, Airport '77—1977, Rollercoaster—1977, House Calls—1978, Nunzio—1978, Airport '79/The Concorde—1979, Little Miss Marker—1980, The Nude Bomb—1980, Sting II—1982

LARSON, Bob Office: Universal Studios
   100 Universal City Plaza
   Universal City, CA 91608
   Telephone: (213) 508-2843

credits: FM—1978, 9-30-55—1979, Coal Miner's Daughter *(exec. prod.)*—1980, Continental Divide—1981

LAZARUS, Paul
   Attorney: Norman Garey
   Rosenfeld, Meyer, & Sussman
   Beverly Hills, CA 90210
   Telephone: (213 858-7700

credits: Extreme Close Up—1971, Westworld—1973, Futureworld—1975, Capricorn 1—1978, Hanover Street—1979, Barbarosa—1982

LEIDER, Jerry
(see also Producers, Movies for TV)
   Warner Hollywood Studios
   1041 N. Formosa Ave.
   Los Angeles, CA 90046

credits: The Jazz Singer—1980, Trenchcoat—1982

LEVINE, Joseph E.
   Business: Joseph E. Levine Presents
   277 Park Avenue
   New York City, NY 10017
   Telephone: (212) 956-5600

credits: The Graduate—1967, The Lion in Winter—1968, The Producers—1968, Sunflower—1970, Soldier Blue—1970, Carnal Knowledge—1971, Day of the Dolphin—1973, A Bridge Too Far—1977, Magic—1978, Tattoo—1981

LEVY, Franklin R.
(see also Producers, Movies for TV)
   Business: Catalina Prod. Group, Ltd.
   The Burbank Studios
   4000 Warner Boulevard
   Burbank, CA 91522
   Telephone: (213) 954-6447

credits: Nighthawks *(executive producer with Mike Wise)*—1981

LINSON, Art
   Universal Studios, Bldg. 84
   Universal City, CA 91608
   Telephone: (213) 508-1581

credits: Rafferty and the Gold Dust Twins—1975, Carwash—1976, American Hot Wax—1978, Melvin and Howard *(coproduced with Don Phillips)*—1980

LITTO, George
   Office: 1875 Century Park East
   Suite 600
   Los Angeles, CA 90067
   Telephone: (213) 278-0017

credits: Over the Edge—1978, Drive In—1976, Obsession—1979, Dressed to Kill—1980, Blowout—1981

LOBELL, Michael
   Business: Warner Bros.
   4000 Warner Boulevard
   Burbank, CA 91522
   Telephone: (213) 954-6000

LOBELL, Michael, *continued*

credits: So Fine *(co-produced with Andrew Bergman)*—1981

LOVELL, Dyson

credits: Endless Love—1981

LUCAS, George
Business: Lucasfilm, Ltd.
P.O. Box 2009
San Rafael, CA 94912
Telephone: (415) 457-5282

credits: More American Graffitti—1979, The Empire Strikes Back—1980, Raiders of the Lost Ark—1981, Revenge of the Jedi—[in production] *(all as Executive Producer)*

MANES, Fritz
Business: The Malpaso Co.
4000 Warner Boulevard
Burbank, CA 91522
Telephone: (213) 954-2567

credits: Any Which Way You Can—1981

MARSHALL, Frank
Agent: Creative Artists Agency
1888 Century Park East, Suite 1400
Los Angeles, CA 90067
Telephone: (213) 277-4545

credits: Raiders of the Lost Ark—1981

McEUEN, William E.
Business: Aspen Film Society
7958 Beverly Boulevard
Beverly Hills, CA 90210
Telephone: (213) 655-8950

credits: The Jerk *(co-produced with David Picker)*—1979, Dead Men Don't Wear Plaid *(with Picker)*—1982

McNAMARA, James J.
Business: H.W.C. Inc.
Palm Beach, Florida

credits: Hardly Working—1981

MELNICK, Dan
Business: The IndieProd Co.
10201 West Pico Blvd.
Los Angeles, CA 90035
Telephone: (213) 203-3241

credits: Straw Dogs—1971, That's Entertainment!—1974, That's Entertainment, Part 2 *(co-produced with Saul Chaplin(*—1976, All That Jazz—1979, The First Family—1981, Altered States—1981, Making Love—1982, Unfaithfully Yours—1983

MERCHANT, Ismail
Business: Merchant Ivory Prod's, Ltd.
250 West 57th St., Suite 1913-A
New York, NY 10019

credits: Autobiography of a Princess—1975, Roseland—1977, Hullabaloo Over Georgie and Bonnies Pictures—1978, The Europeans—1979, The 5:48—1979, Jane Austen in Manhattan—1980, Quartet—1981

MERRICK, David
246 West 44th Street
New York, NY 10036
Telephone: (212) 563-7520

credits: Child's Play—1972, The Great Gatsby—1974, Semi-Tough—1977, Rough Cut—1978

MICHAELS, Joel B. and DRABINSKY, Garth
credits: Tribute—1980

MILCHAN, Arnon
Business: Regency Films
80 East 11th Street
New York, NY 10003
Telephone: (212) 460-5072

credits: The King of Comedy—[not yet released], Once Upon a Time in America—[upcoming]

producers, motion picture

MILLER, Ron
Business: Walt Disney Productions
500 South Buena Vista Street
Burbank, CA 91521
Telephone: (213) 840-1000
credits: Tron—1981, Tex—1982, Trench-coat *(as Executive Producer)*—1982

MIRISCH, Marvin
MIRISCH, Walter
Business: The Mirisch Corporation
3966 Overland Avenue
Culver City, CA 90230
Telephone: (213) 202-0202
credits: In the Heat of the Night—1967, The Thomas Crown Affair—1968, The Organization—1970, The Hawaiians—1970, The Private Life of Sherlock Holmes—1970, They Call Me Mr. Tibbs—1970, The Landlord—1970, Scorpio—1972, Mr. Majestyk, The Spikes Gang—1974, Midway—1976, Same Time Next Year—1978, Midway—197?, Dracula—1979

MISSEL, Renee
Business: Missel Productions
100 Universal City Plaza
Universal City, CA 91608
Telephone: (213) 985-4321
credits: The Main Event—1978, Resurrection *(with Howard Rosenman)*—1980

MONASH, Paul
Agent: Hal Ross, Wm. Morris Agency
151 El Camino Drive
Beverly Hills, CA 90212
Telephone: (213) 274-7451
credits: Butch Cassidy and the Sundance Kid—1969, Slaughterhouse Five—1972, The Friends of Eddie Coyle—1973, The Front Page—1974, Carrie—1976

MOONJEAN, Hank
The Burbank Studios, Bldg. 25
4000 Warner Boulevard
Burbank, CA 91522
Telephone: (213) 954-6000

credits: The Fortune *(as executive producer)*—1975, The End *(as executive producer)*—1977, The Beauty and the Beast—1978, Hooper—1978, Smokey and the Bandit, Part II—1980, The Incredible Shrinking Woman—1981, Paternity *(co-produced with Lawrence Gordon)*—1981, Sharkey's Machine—1981

MURPHY, Michael
Business: Michael Murphy Productions
6363 Wilshire Boulevard
Los Angeles, CA 90048
Telephone: (213) 655-4879
credits: St. Helens *(exec. prod.)*—1981, O'Hara's Wife *(exec. prod.)*—[upcoming]

PALEVSKY, Max and
BART, Peter
credits: Fun with Dick and Jane—1977, Islands in the Stream—1977

PANZER, William and
DAVIS, Peter
Business: Davis-Panzer Productions
Sunset-Gower Studios
1438 North Gower Street
Hollywood, CA 90028
Telephone: (213) 463-2343
credits: The Death Collector—1977, Stunts *(as co-producer)*—1978, Steel—1979, St. Helens *(co-produced with Peter Davis)*—1981, O'Hara's Wife *(as co-producer)*—1982, The Jupiter Menace *(as co-executive producer)*—1982, The Osterman Weekend *(co-produced with Davis)*—1983

PAPP, Joseph
Business: The New York Shakespeare
Festival
425 Lafayette Street
New York, NY 10023
Telephone: (212) 598-7148
credits: Over the Edge—1978, The Pirates of Penzance *(with Edward R. Pressman)*—1982

PERSKY, Lester
Business: Lester Persky Productions
555 Madison Avenue
New York, NY 10022
Telephone: (213) 421-4141
935 Bel Air Drive
Los Angeles, CA

credits: The Last Detail—1973, For Pete's Sake—1974, Bite the Bullet—1975, The Killer Elite—1975, The Man Who Would Be King—1975, Shampoo—1975, The Front—1976, Taxi Driver—1976, The Missouri Breaks—1976, Bound For Glory—1977, Equus—1977, Hair—1978, Yanks—1979, Bent—[upcoming]

PETERS, Jon
Business: The Jon Peters
          Organization
301 N. Carolwood
Los Angeles, CA 90024
Telephone: (213) 274-7801

credits: A Star Is Born—1976, The Eyes of Laura Mars—1978, Caddyshack—1980, An American Werewolf in London *(as executive producer with Peter Guber)*—1981, Missing *(as executive producer with Guber)*—1982

PHILLIPS, Julia
Business: Ruthless Films
10202 W. Washington Boulevard
Culver City, CA 90230

credits: Steelyard Blues—1972, The Sting—1973, Taxi Driver—1976, Close Encounters of the Third Kind—1977

(Co-produced with Michael Phillips)

PHILLIPS, Michael
Business: Universal Studios
Universal City, CA 91608
Telephone: (213) 508-2938

credits (with Julia Phillips): Steelyard Blues—1972, The Sting—1973, Taxi Driver—1976, Close Encounters of the Third Kind—1977; *(without Julia Phillips)* Cannery Row—1981, Heartbeeps—1981

PICKER, David
Aspen Film Society
7958 Beverly Boulevard
Telephone: (213) 655-8950

credits: Lenny—1974, Juggernaut—1974, Royal Flash—1975, Smile—1975, Oliver's Story—1978, The One and Only—1978

POLL, Martin
Business: Martin Poll Productions
919 Third Avenue
New York, NY 10019
Telephone: (212) 371-7175

credits: Love Is a Ball—1962, Sylvia—1964, The Appointment—1968, The Lion In Winter—1968, The Magic Garden of Stanley Sweetheart—1970, Night Watch—1972, The Man Who Loved Cat Dancing—1973, Love and Death—1975, The Sailor Who Fell From Grace With the Sea—1976, Somebody Killed Her Husband—1978, Night Hawks—1981

PRATT, Charles A., Sr.
Comworld Productions
15301 Ventura Boulevard
Sherman Oaks, CA 91403
Telephone: (213) 907-1450

credits—(as executive producer): Willard—1971, Ben—1972, You'll Like My Mother—1972, Walking Tall—1973, Terror in the Wax Museum—1973, Arnold—1973, Walking Tall, Part II—1975, The Reincarnation of Peter Proud—1975, Special Delivery—1976; *(as producer):* Walking Tall: The Final Chapter—1977, Mean Dog Blues—1978, The Great Santini—1979

PRESSMAN, Edward
Business: Edward R. Pressman
          Productions

PRESSMAN, Edward, *continued*

The Burbank Studios
4000 Warner Boulevard
Burbank, CA 91522
Telephone: (213) 954-6000

credits: Out Of It—1969, The Revolutionary—1970, Dealing—1972, Sisters—1973, Badlands—1973, Phantom of the Paradise—1974, Despair—1977, Nunzio—1978, Paradise Alley—1978, Heart Beat—1979, The Hand—1981, Das Boot—1982, Flicks—1982, Conan *(with Dino De Laurentiis)*—1982, The Pirates of Penzance *(with Joseph Papp)*—[upcoming]

PUTTNAM, David

Business: Enigma Overseas Variations
The Burbank Studios
4000 Warner Boulevard
Burbank, CA 91522
Telephone: (213) 954-3673

credits: Stardust—1975, Bugsy Malone—1976, The Duellists—1978, Midnight Express—1978, Chariots of Fire *(Academy Award–Best Picture)*—1981, Local Hero—1983

RADNITZ, Robert

3954 Overland Avenue, Suite 204
Culver City, CA 90230
Telephone: (213) 558-6195

credits: A Dog of Flanders—1960, Misty—1961, Island of Blue Dolphins—1965, And Now Miguel—1966, My Side of the Mountain—1969, The Little Ark—1972, Sounder—1972, Where the Lilies Bloom—1974, Birch Interval—1976, Sounder II—19__, A Hero Ain't Nothin' But a Sandwich—1977, Cross Creek—1982

RAFELSON, Bob
(see also Directors)

Business: 1400 North Fuller Ave.
Los Angeles, CA 90046

credits (co-produced with Bert Schneider & Steve Blauner): Head—1968, Easy Rider—1969, Five Easy Pieces—1970, Drive, He Said—1970, The Last Picture Show—1971, A Safe Place—1971, The King of Marvin Gardens—1972, Hearts and Minds—1974, Stay Hungry—1976; *(co-produced with Charles Mulvehill)* The Postman Always Rings Twice—1981

RANSOHOFF, Martin

Business: Martin Ransohoff
Productions
300 Colgems Square
Burbank, CA 91505
Telephone: (213) 954-6000

credits: The Sandpiper—1965, The Cincinnati Kid—1965, Ice Station Zebra—1968, Castle Keep—1968, Catch-22—1970, The Moonshine War—1970, Save the Tiger—1972, The White Dawn—1973, The Silver Streak—1977, The Other Side of Midnight—1977, The Invasion of the Body Snatchers—1978, Nightwing—1978, The Wanderers—1979, A Change of Seasons—1981, Hanky Panky—1982

REITMAN, Ivan

Office: Columbia Pictures
300 Colgems Square
Burbank, CA 91505
Telephone: (213) 954-1771

credits: National Lampoon's Animal House *(co-produced with Matty Simmons)*—1978, Stripes *(co-produced with Dan Goldberg)*—1981

**RICHARDS, Martin and
JOHNSON, Mary Lea**

Business: Producer Circle Co.
9200 Sunset Blvd., Suite 920
Los Angeles, CA 90069
Telephone: (213) 278-1422

New York address:
1350 Avenue of the Americas
New York, NY 100__
Telephone: 212) 765-6760

credits: Fort Apache: The Bronx—1981

ROBERTS, Bobby

credits: The Gypsy Moths—1969, Monte Walsh—1970, The Hot Rock—1972, Death Wish—1974, Joyride—1977, August Is a Wicked Month, Death Wish II—1982

ROBERTSON, Robbie

credits: The Last Waltz—1978, Carney—1980

ROLLINS, Jack, and
JOFFE, Charles H.

Main Office: Rollins-Joffe-Morra-Brezner Productions
130 West 57th Street
New York, NY 10019
Telephone: (212) 582-1940

Offices: Paramount Pictures
5555 Melrose Avenue
Los Angeles, CA 90038
Telephone: (213) 468-5000

credits: Take the Money and Run—1969, Bananas—1971, Everything You Always Wanted to Know About Sex—1972, Sleeper—1973, Love and Death—1975, Annie Hall—1977, Interiors—1978, Manhattan—1979, Stardust Memories—1980

ROOS, Fred and
FREDERICKSON, Gray

Office: Zoetrope Studios
1040 North Las Palmas
Los Angeles, CA 90038
Telephone: (213) 463-7191

credits: Apocalypse Now—1979, Hammet—[not yet released], One from the Heart—1982, The Outsiders—1982

ROSE, Alex and
ASSEYEV, Tamara

Office: MGM Studios
10202 W. Washington Boulevard
Culver City, CA 90230
Telephone: (213) 558-6470

credits: Drive In—1977, Big Wednesday

(as Exec. Producers))—1978, I Wanna Hold Your Hand—1978, Norma Rae—1979

ROSEN, Robert L.

Office: CBS Theatrical Films
Studio Center
4024 Radford Avenue
Studio City, CA 91604
Telephone: (213) 760-6161

credits: The Prophecy—1979, French Connection II—1975, Black Sunday—1977, The Challenge—1982

ROSENMAN, Howard

Bus.: Howard Rosenman Productions
5555 Melrose Avenue
Los Angeles, CA 90038
Telephone: (213) 468-5000

credits: Sparkle—1976, The Main Event (executive producer with Renee Missel)—1978, Resurrection (co-produced with Renee Missel)—1980

ROTH, Richard

Office: Warner Bros.
4000 Warner Boulevard
Burbank, CA 91522
Telephone: (213) 954-6622

credits: Julia—1977

RUDDY, Albert S.

Business: Albert Ruddy Productions
Warners Hollywood Studios
1041 North Formosa Avenue
Los Angeles, CA 90046
Telephone: (213) 650-2514

credits: Little Fauss and Big Halsey—1970, The Godfather—1972, The Longest Yard—1975, Coonskin—1975, Matilda—1978, Cannonball Run—1980, Death Hunt (as executive producer)—1981, Megaforce—1982

producers, motion picture

RUSSO, Aaron
Business: Aaron Russo Productions
5555 Melrose Avenue
Los Angeles, CA 90038
Telephone: (213) 468-5000
credits: The Rose *(co-produced with Marvin Worth)*—1979, Partners—1982

RYDELL, Mark
Business: Mark Rydell Productions
100 Universal Plaza
Universal City, CA 91608
Telephone: (213) 508-0308
credits: Cinderella Liberty—1973, Harry and Walter Go to New York—1975

SACKHEIM, William
Office: Rastar Films
300 Colgems Square
Burbank, CA 91505
Telephone: (213) 954-6000
credits: The Competition—1980, No Small Affair—1981

SALKIND, Ilya and Alexander
Contact: Warner House
London, England
Telephone: 011-44-753-654-545
credits: The Light at the Edge of the World—1971, The Three Musketeers—1973, The Four Musketeers—1974, Superman—1978, Superman II—1981

SANGER, Jonathan
Office: Brooksfilms, Ltd.
1040 North Las Palmas
Los Angeles, CA 90038
Telephone: (213) 460-7044
credits: The Elephant Man—1980, The Francis Farmer Story *(co-produced with Marie Yates)—1982*

SCHAFFEL, Robert
Office: CBS Theatrical Films
4024 Radford Avenue
Studio City, CA 91604
Business: Voight/Schaffel Prod's.
The Burbank Studios
Columbia Plaza, Burbank 91505
Telephone: (213) 954-3411
credits: Table For Five—1983, The Raoul Wallenberg Story *(with John Voight)*—[upcoming]

SCHERICK, Edgar
Business: Edgar J. Scherick
Associates
3400 W. Alameda Ave., Suite 200
Burbank, CA 91505
Telephone: (213) 841-4913
credits: I'm Dancing as Fast as I Can—1982, Shoot the Moon—1982

SCHNEER, Charles H.
credits: The 7th Voyage of Sinbad—1958, The Three Worlds of Gulliver—1960, I Aim at the Stars—1960, The Executioner—1970, The Golden Voyage of Sinbad—1974, Sinbad and the Eye of the Tiger—1977, Clash of the Titans—1981

SCHWARTZ, Bernard
Office: Universal Studios
100 Universal City Plaza
Universal City, CA 91608
Telephone: (213) 985-4321
credits: Coal Miner's Daughter—1980

SCHWARY, Ronald L.
Business: RLS Productions
Laird International Studios
9336 West Washington Blvd.
Culver City, CA 90230
Telephone: (213) 836-5537
credits: The Electric Horseman—1978, Ordinary People—1980, Absence of Malice *(executive producer)*—1981, Tootsie *(executive producer)*—1983

SELLERS, Arlene, and
WINITSKY, Alex
Business: Film Funding Corporation
9720 Wilshire Boulevard
Beverly Hills, CA 90212
Telephone: (213) 274-2761
credits: Don't Look Now—1975, Silver
Bears—1977, House Calls—1978, Cuba—
1979

SHAGAN, Steve
(see also Screenwriters)
Agent: Creative Artists Agency
1888 Century Park East, Suite 1400
Los Angeles, CA 90067
Telephone: (213) 277-4545
credits: Save the Tiger—1972, Voyage of
the Damned—1977, The Formula—1980

SHEPHERD, Richard
Business: The Richard Shepherd Co.
MGM Studios
10202 W. Washington Boulevard
Culver City, CA 90230
Telephone: (213) 558-6506
credits: Twelve Angry Men—1957, The
Hanging Tree—1959, The Fugitive Kind—
1960, Breakfast At Tiffany's—1961, Alex
and the Gypsy—19__, Robin and Marian—
1976, The Hunger—1983

SHUSETT, Ronald
credits: Alien—1979, Dead and Buried
(with Robert Fentress)—1981

SIMMONS, Matty
Business: National Lampoon
9301 Wilshire Blvd., Suite 412
Beverly Hills, CA 90210
Telephone: (213) 859-8834
credits: National Lampoon's Animal
House—1978, National Lampoon Goes to
the Movies—[not yet released]

SIMON, Melvin
Business: Simon/Reeves/Landsburg
260 South Beverly Drive
Beverly Hills, CA 90212
Telephone: (213) 273-5450
credits—(as Executive Producer): Love At
First Bite—1978, My Bodyguard—1980,
Porky's *(co-producer)*—1982

SIMON, Neil
(see also Screenwriters)
Office: Los Angeles, CA 90046
Telephone: (213) 650-2500
credits: Only When I Laugh, I Ought to Be
in Pictures

SOLO, Robert
Business: Solo Film Company
1041 North Formosa Avenue
Los Angeles, CA 90046
Telephone: (213) 650-2592
credits: Invasion of the Body Snatchers—
1978, The Awakening—1980, I, the Jury—
1981

SPANGLER, Larry
credits: Chanel Solitaire—1981

SPIELBERG, Steven
(see also Directors)
Business: Amblin Productions
MGM Studios
10202 West Washington Blvd.
Culver City, CA 90230
Telephone: (213) 558-5000
credits: Used Cars—1980, *(as exec.*
prod.) Poltergeist—1982, E.T.—1982

STARGER, Martin
Office: Marble Arch Productions
4024 Radford Avenue, Bldg. 2
Studio City, CA 91604
Telephone: (213) 760-6101
credits: Movie, Movie—1978, From the
Life of the Marionettes—1979, The Mup-
pet Movie—1979, Autumn Sonata—1979,

producers, motion picture

STARGER, Martin, *continued*
Raise the Titanic—1980, Saturn 3—1980, The Last Unicorn—1981, Barbarosa—1981, The Great Muppet Caper—1981, Hard Country—1981, Sophie's Choice—1982 *(All as Executive Producer)*

STARK, Ray
  Business: Rastar Films, Inc.
  300 Colgems Square
  Burbank, CA 91505
  Telephone: (213) 843-6000

credits: Reflections in a Golden Eye—1970, The Owl and The Pussycat—1972, Fat City—1973, The Way We Were—1973, Funny Lady—1975, The Sunshine Boys—1975, Murder by Death—1976, Smokey and the Bandit—1977, The Goodbye Girl—1978, The Cheap Detective—1978, California Suite—1978, Chapter Two—1979, The Electric Horseman—1979, The Hunter—1980, Seems Like Old Times—1980, Annie—1981, Death at an Early Age—[upcoming]

STIGWOOD, Robert
  Business: 1775 Broadway
  New York, NY 10019
  Telephone: (212) 975-0700
  5555 Melrose Avenue
  Los Angeles, CA 90038
  Telephone: (213) 466-5000

credits: Jesus Christ, Superstar—1973, Tommy—1975, Survive—1976, Bugsy Malone—1976, Saturday Night Fever—1977, Grease—1978, Moment by Moment—1978, Sergeant Pepper's Lonely Hearts Club Band—1978, Times Square—1980, Gallipoli—1981, The Fan—1981, Young Lust *(with George Van Noy)*—1981, Grease 2 *(co-produced with Allan Carr)*—1982, Evita—[not yet released]

SUSSKIND, David
  Business: The Susskind Company
  1350 Avenue of the Stars
  New York, NY 10019
  Telephone: (212) 765-0505

MGM Studios
10202 West Washington Boulevard
Culver City, CA 90230
Telephone: (213) 558-5000

credits: A Raisin in the Sun—1961, Lovers and Other Strangers—1969, All Creatures Great and Small—1974, Alice Doesn't Live Here Anymore—1974, Buffalo Bill and the Indians—1976

TANNEN, Michael
credits: One-Trick Pony—1980

TENSER, Marilyn
  Crown International Pictures
  292 South La Cienega Blvd.
  Beverly Hills, CA 90211
  Telephone: (213) 657-6700

credits: Beach Girls—1982

TISCH, Steve and
AVNET, Jon
  see also Producers, Movies for TV
  Business: Tisch/Avnet Productions, Inc.
  515 North Robertson Boulevard
  Los Angeles, CA 90048
  Telephone: (213) 278-7680

credits: Coast to Coast—1980

TRIKILIS, Michael
  Office: Twentiety Century-Fox
  10201 West Pico Blvd.
  Los Angeles, CA 90035

credits: Six Pack—1982

TURMAN, Lawrence
  Business: Turman-Foster Company
  100 Universal City Plaza
  Universal City, CA 91608
  Telephone: (213) 508-3182

credits: The Flim Flam Man—1967, The Graduate—1969, Pretty Poison—1970, The Great White Hope—1971, The Marriage of a Young Stockbroker—1975, The Drowning Pool—1977, First Love—1977,

producers, motion picture

TURMAN, Lawrence, *continued*
Heroes—1977, Tribute—1980, Caveman—1981, The Thing—1982, Second Thoughts—1982, Charmed Lives—[upcoming]

UBAUD, Jean and
EDELMAN, Kate
Business: Edelman-Ubaud Productions
9901 Durant Drive
Beverly Hills, CA 90212
Telephone: (213) 557-1917

credits: TAG: The Assassination Game—1981

VALENTE, Renée
(see also Producers, Movies for TV)
Twentieth Century-Fox Television
P.O. Box 900
Beverly Hills, CA 90213
Telephone: (213) 277-2211

credits: Loving Couples—1980

WEINSTEIN, Hannah
Office: Columbia Pictures
300 Colgems Square
Burbank, CA 91505
Telephone: (213) 954-6000

credits: Greased Lightning—1977, Stir Crazy—1981, Deep Trouble—[upcoming]

WEINTRAUB, Fred
Business: Fred Weintraub Productions
12655 Washington Blvd., Suite 202
Los Angeles, CA 90066
Telephone: (213) 390-7636

credits: Rage—1972, Enter the Dragon *(with Paul Heller)*—1973, Black Belt Jones—1974, Golden Needles—1974, Truck Turner—1974, Outlaw Blues—1977, The Promise—1979, Tom Horn—1980, The Big Brawl—1980, Force: Five—1981, High Road to China—1983

WEINTRAUB, Jerry
Management Three
9744 Wilshire Boulevard
Beverly Hills, CA 90212
Telephone: (213) 550-7100

credits: Nashville—1975, Oh God!—1977, 9/30/55—197__, Cruising—1980, All Night Long—1981, Diner—1982

WEISSBOURD, Burt
Weissbourd Films
Universal Studios
100 Universal City Plaza
Universal City, CA 91608
Telephone: (213) 208-6722

credits: Raggedy Man—1981, Ghost Story—1982

WESTON, Jay
3940 Overland Avenue, Suite 207
Culver City, CA 90230
Telephone: (213) 202-4425

credits: Lady Sings the Blues—1972, W. C. Fields and Me—1976, Night of the Juggler—1979, Buddy Buddy—1981, Chu Chu and the Philly Flash—1981

WILLOUGHBY, George
credits: Boardwalk—1979

WINITSKY, Alex and
SELLERS, Arlene
Business: Film Funding Corporation
9720 Wilshire Boulevard
Beverly Hills, CA 90212
Telephone: (213) 274-2761

credits: Don't Look Now—1975, Silver Bears—1977, House Calls—1978, Cuba—1979

WINKLER, Irwin and
CHARTOFF, Robert
Business: Chartoff-Winkler
    Productions, Inc.
10125 W. Washington Blvd.
Culver City, CA 90230
Telephone: (213) 204-0474

WINKLER- CHARTOFF, *continued*

credits: The Split—1968, Leo the Last—1969, They Shoot Horses, Don't They?—1969, The Strawberry Statement—1970, The Gang that Couldn't Shoot Straight—1971, The New Centurions—1972, Up the Sandbox—1972, The Mechanic—1972, S*P*Y*S—1974, Peeper—1975, The Gambler—1975, Rocky—1976, Nickelodeon—1976, New York, New York—1977, Sons—1978, Comes A Horseman—1978, Rocky II—1979, Raging Bull—1980, True Confessions—1981, Rocky III—1982

WISE, Robert
Business: Robert Wise Productions
Sunset Gower Studios
1438 North Gower Street, Suite 562
Hollywood, CA 90028
Telephone: (213) 461-3864

credits: Odds Against Tomorrow—1959, West Side Story—1961, The Haunting—1963, The Sound of Music—1965, The Sand Pebbles, 1966, Star!—1968, The Andromeda Strain—1971, Two People—1973, The Hindenburg—1975,

WIZAN, Joseph
CBS Theatrical Films Div.
4024 Radford Avenue
Studio City, CA 91604
Telephone: (213) 760-5000

credits: Junior Bonner—1972, Jeremiah Johnson—1972, Prime Cut—1972, The Last American Hero—1973, 99 and 44/100 Per Cent Dead—1974, Audrey Rose—1977, Voices—1979, And Justice for All—1979, Best Friends *(as executive producer)*—1982

WORTH, Marvin
Business: Marvin Worth Productions
The Burbank Studios
4000 Warner Boulevard
Burbank, CA 91522
Telephone: (213) 954-3651

credits—(as co-producer): Where's Poppa—1970, The Rose—1979, Up the Academy—1980; *(as producer):* Malcolm X—1972, Lenny—1974, Firesale—1976, Soup For One—1981

YABLANS, Frank
Business: Frank Yablans Productions
10201 West Pico Boulevard
Los Angeles, CA 90064
Telephone: (213) 277-2211

credits: The Silver Streak—1977, The Other Side of Midnight—1977, The Fury—1978, North Dallas Forty—1979, Mommie Dearest—1981

YABLANS, Irwin
Business: Compass International Films
9229 West Sunset Boulevard
Los Angeles, CA 90069
Telephone: (213) 273-9125

credits: The Education of Sonny Carson—1974, Halloween *(as executive producer)*—1978, Roller Boogie—1978, Fade to Black *(as executive producer)*—1979, Hell Night—1981, The Seduction *(with Bruce Curtis)*—1982

ZANUCK, Richard and
BROWN, David
Business: Zanuck/Brown Co.
P.O. Box 900
Beverly Hills, CA 90213
Telephone: (213) 203-3215

credits: The Sting—1973, The Sugarland Express—1974, Jaws—1977, MacArthur—1977, Jaws II-1978, The Island—1979, Neighbors—1981, The Verdict—1982

ZINNEMANN, Tim
credits: Straight Time—1978, A Small Circle of Friends—1979, The Long Riders—1980, Tex—1982

SCREENWRITERS

ABRAHAMS, Jim
(see also Directors)
c/o Terry Shagin, Esq.
11777 San Vicente Blvd., Suite 600
Los Angeles, CA 90049

credits (with David and Jerry Zucker):
Kentucky Fried Movie—1977, Airplane—1980

ALDA, Alan
(see also Directors)
Office: Twentiety Century-Fox Studios
10201 West Pico Boulevard
Los Angeles, CA 90035
Telephone: (213) 203-3168

credits: The Seduction of Joe Tynan—1979, The Four Seasons—1981

ALLEN, Chris
Agent: Merrilly Kane Agency
9171 Wilshire Blvd., Suite 507
Beverly Hills, CA 90210
Telephone: (213) 550-8874

credits: The Last Remake of Beau Geste—1977, In God We Trust *(with Marty Feldman)*—1979

ALLEN, Jay Presson
Agent: ICM
8899 Beverly Boulevard
Los Angeles, CA 90048
Telephone: (213) 550-4000

credits: Cabaret—1971, Travels with my Aunt—1972, 40 Carats—1973, Funny Lady—1974, Just Tell Me What You Want—1979, The Verdict—1981, Deathtrap—1982

ALLEN, Woody
(see also Directors)
Contact: Rollins/Joffe/Morra/Brezner
New York, NY 10019
Telephone: (212) 582-1940

credits: Take the Money and Run—1969, Bananas—1971, Play It Again Sam—1972, Everything You Always Wanted to Know about Sex—1973, Sleeper *(with Marshall Brickman)*—1973, Love and Death—1975, Annie Hall *(with Marshall Brickman)*—1977, Interiors—1978, Manhattan *(with Marshall Brickman)*—1979, Stardust Memories—1980, A Midsummer Night's Sex Comedy—1982

ALTMAN, Robert
(see also Directors)
Agent: ICM
40 West 57th Street
New York, NY 10019
Telephone: (212) 556-5600

Business: Landscape Films
12115 Magnolia Blvd., Suite 123
North Hollywood, CA 91607
Telephone: (213) 509-0259

credits: McCabe and Mrs. Miller—1971, Images—1972, Thieves Like Us *(with Joan Tewkesbury and Calder Willingham)*—1973, Buffalo Bill and the Indians—1976, Three Women—1976, A Wedding *(with John Considine)*—1977, Quintet *(with Frank Barhydt and Patricia Resnick)*-1978, A Perfect Couple—1978, Health *(with Paul Dooley and Frank Barhydt)*—1979

AMBROSE, David
Agent: The Paul Kohner Agency
9169 Sunset Boulevard
Los Angeles, CA 90069
Telephone: (213) 550-1050

credits: The Final Countdown—1979

ANHALT, Edward
Agent: The Paul Kohner Agency
9169 Sunset Boulevard
Los Angeles, CA 90069
Telephone: (213) 550-1050

credits: Panic in the Streets—1950, Not As A Stranger—1955, The Pride and the Passion—1957, The Young Lions—1958, Beckett—1964, The Boston Strangler—1968, The Madwoman of Chaillot—1969,

ANHALT, *continued*
Jeremiah Johnson—1971, Luther—1973, The Man in the Glass Booth—1975, Escape to Athena—1978, Splendora *(with Camilla Carr)*—[upcoming]

APPET, Leah
Business: Hickmar Productions
4000 Warner Boulevard
Burbank, CA 91522
Telephone: (213) 954-6000
Agent: Robinson-Weintraub Assoc.

credits: The Fifth Floor *(with Howard Avedis)*—1979, Separate Ways—1981

AVEDIS, Howard
(see also Directors)
Office: Warner Bros. Producers Bldg.
4000 Warner Boulevard
Burbank, CA 91522
Telephone: (213) 954-6000

credits: The Fifth Floor—1979, Separate Ways *(with Leah Appet)*—1979

AYRES, Gerald
Agent: William Morris Agency
151 El Camino Drive
Beverly Hills, CA 90212
Telephone: (213) 274-7451
credits: Foxes—1979, Rich and Famous—1981

BAUM, Thomas
Agent: Sanford-Beckett Agbency
1015 Gayley Avenue, Suite 301
Los Angeles, CA 90024
credits: Carny—1979

BEATTY, Warren
(see also Directors)
Office: Paramount Pictures
Telephone: (213) 468-5000

credits: Shampoo *(with Robert Towne)*—1974, Heaven Can Wait—*(with Elaine May)*—1978, Reds *(with Trevor Griffiths)*—1981

BELSON, Jerry
(see also Directors)
Manager: Shapiro-West
141 El Camino Drive
Beverly Hills, CA 90210
Telephone: (213) 278-8896

credits: The Grasshopper—1969, Smile—1974, Fun with Dick and Jane—1976, The End—1977, Smokey and the Bandit II—1980, Jekyll & Hyde ... Together Again—1982

BENCHLEY, Peter
Agent: ICM
40 West 57th Street
New York, NY 10019
Telephone: (212) 586-5100

credits: Jaws—1974, The Deep—1977, The Island—1979

BENTON, Robert
Agent: International Creative
      Management
40 West 57th Street
New York, NY 10019
Telephone: (212) 556-6800

credits: There Was a Crooked Man—1969, What's Up Doc?—1971, Bad Company—1972, The Late Show—1976, Kramer vs. Kramer—1978, Superman—1978, Stab—1982

BERGMAN, Andrew
Agent: Adams, Ray & Rosenberg
9200 Sunset Boulevard
Los Angeles, CA 90069
Telephone: (213) 278-3000

credits: Blazing Saddles *(with Mel Brooks)*—1973, The In-Laws—1979, So Fine—1981

BERGREN, Eric
Agent: Sanford-Beckett Agency
1015 Gayley Avenue, Suite 301
Los Angeles, CA 90024
Telephone: (213) 208-2100

BERGREN, Eric, *continued*
credits: The Elephant Man *(with Christopher DeVore)*—1980, The Francis Farmer Story *(with Christopher De Vore)*—

BERNSTEIN, B. Armyan
Office: The Burbank Studios
4000 Warner Boulevard
Burbank, CA 91522
Telephone: (213) 954-6464
Agent: Creative Artists Agency
1888 Century Park East, Suite 1400
Los Angeles, CA 90067
Telephone: (213) 277-4545

credits: Thank God It's Friday—1977, One From the Heart *(with Frances Coppola)*—1981

BERNSTEIN, Walter
Agent: ICM
40 West 57th Street
New York, NY 10019
Telephone: (212) 556-5600

credits: The Front—1976, Semi-Tough—1977, The Betsy *(with William Bast)*—1977, An Almost Perfect Affair *(with Don Peterson)*—1979, Little Miss Marker—1979, Yanks—1979

BIRKIN, Andrew
credits: The Final Conflict—1981

BLATTY, William Peter
Agent: William Morris Agency
151 El Camino Drive
Beverly Hills, CA 90212
Telephone: (213) 274-7451

credits: Darling Lili—1969, The Great Bank Robbery—1969, The Exorcist—1972, Twinkle, Twinkle, Killer Kane—1979

BOAM, Jeffrey
Agent: Sanford-Beckett Agency
1015 Gayley Avenue, Suite 301
Los Angeles, CA 90024
Telephone: (213) 208-2100

credits: Straight Time *(with Alvin Sargent and Edward Bunker)*—1977, The Dead Zone—1981

BOBRICK, Sam
Agent: Creative Artists Agency
1888 Century Park East, Suite 1400
Los Angeles, CA 90067
Telephone: (213) 277-4545
Office: Warner Bros.
4000 Warner Boulevard
Burbank, CA 91522
Telephone: (213) 954-4000

credits: Norman, Is That You? *(with Ron Clark)*—1976, The Last Remake of Beau Geste—1977, Jimmy the Kid—1981

BOLOTIN, Craig
Agent: Adams, Ray & Rosenberg
9200 Sunset Blvd., Penthouse 25
Los Angeles, CA 90069
Telephone: (213) 278-3000

credits: No Small Affair—1981

BOLT, Robert
Contact: Embassy Pictures
956 Seward Street
Los Angeles, CA 90038

credits: Lawrence of Arabia—1962, Doctor Zhivago—1965, A Man for all Seasons—1967, A Wrinkle in Time—[upcoming]

BRACH, Gerald
credits: Tess *(with Roman Polanski & John Brownjohn)*—1981, Quest for Fire—1981

BREST, Martin
(see also Directors)
Agent: The Ufland Agency
190 North Canon Dr., Suite 202
Beverly Hills, CA 90210
Telephone: (213) 273-9441

credits: Hot Tomorrows—1977, Going in Style—1979

screenwriters

BRICKMAN, Marshall
(see also Directors)
Agent: ICM
40 West 57th Street
New York, NY 10019
Telephone (212) 556-5600

credits: Sleeper—1973, Annie Hall—1977, Manhattan—1979, Simon—1980, Lovesick—1982

BRIDGES, James
(see also Directors)
Agent: Creative Artists Agency
1888 Century Park East
Los Angeles, CA 90067
Telephone: (213) 277-4545

credits: The Appaloosa—1966, The Forbin Project—1969, The Baby Maker—1970, Limbo—1972, The Paper Chase—1973, September 30, 1955—1977, The China Syndrome—1978, Urban Cowboy—1980, Mike's Murder—1983

BROOKS, Albert
Agent: Creative Artists Agency
1888 Century Park East, Suite 1400
Los Angeles, CA 90067
Telephone: (213) 277-4545

credits: Real Life—1979, Modern Romance *(with Monica Johnson)*—1981

BROOKS, James L.
Agent: ICM
8899 Beverly Boulevard
Los Angeles, CA 90048
Telephone: (213) 550-4000

credits: Starting Over—1979

BROOKS, Mel
(see also Directors)
Office: Twentieth Century-Fox
10201 West Pico Boulevard
Los Angeles, CA 90035
Telephone: (213) 203-1375

credits: The Producers—1968, The Twelve Chairs—1970, Blazing Saddles

(with Norman Steinberg, Richard Pryor, Andrew Bergman, Alan Uger)—1973, Young Frankenstein *(with Gene Wilder)*—1974, Silent Movie *(with Ron Clark, Rudy DeLuca, and Barry Levinson)*—1976, , High Anxiety—1977, History of the World: Part 1—1981

BROOKS, Richard
(see also Directors)
Attorney: Gerald Lipsky
190 North Canon Drive
Beverly Hills, CA 90210
Telephone: (213) 878-4100
Office: Rastar Films
Telephone: (213) 954-6000

credits: The Happy Ending—1969, Dollar$—1971, Bite the Bullet—1975, Looking for Mr. Goodbar—1977, Wrong Is Right—1982

BURNS, Allan
Agent: Ziegler, Diskant
9255 Sunset Boulevard
Los Angeles, CA 90069
Telephone: (213) 278-0070

credits: Butch and Sundance: The Early Days—1978, A Little Romance—1979

BYRUM, John
Agent: William Morris Agency
151 El Camino Drive
Beverly Hills, CA 90212
Telephone: (213) 274-7451

credits: Heart Beat—1979, Inserts—1976, Harry and Walter Go to New York *(with Robert Kaufman)*—1976, Mahogony—1975

CARLINO, Lewis John
Agent: Creative Artist Agency
1888 Century Park East, Suite 1400
Los Angeles, CA 90067
Telephone: (213) 277-4545

credits: Seconds, The Fox—1968, The Brotherhood, Labyrinth—1971, The Mechanic—1972, Crazy Joe—1973, The

CARLINO, Lewis John, *continued*
Sailor Who Fell From Grace with the Sea—1976, I Never Promised You a Rose Garden—1977, The Great Santini—1978, Resurrection—1979

CARPENTER, John
Agent: Phil Gersh Agency
222 North Canon Drive
Beverly Hills, CA 90210
Telephone: (213) 274-6611

credits: The Eyes of Laura Mars *(with David Z. Goodman)*—1978, Halloween— *(with Debra Hill)*—1978, The Fog—*(with Debra Hill)*—1979, Escape from New York *(with Nick Castle)*—1981, Halloween II *(with Debra Hill)*—1981

CASTLE, Nick
Agent: Rifkin, David, Kimble
Parseghian
7318 Beverly Boulevard
Los Angeles, CA 90036
Telephone: (213) 857-1234

credits: Skatetown U.S.A.—1979, TAG—1981, Escape from New York *(with John Carpenter)*—1981

CHRISTIAN, H. R.
credits: Black Mama, White Mama— 1972, Act of Vengeance—1974, King of the Mountain—1981

CIMINO, Michael
(see also Directors)
Agent: William Morris Agency
151 El Camino Drive
Beverly Hills, CA 90212
Telephone: (213) 274-7451

Office: Laird International Studios
Telephone: (213) 836-5537

credits: Silent Running *(with Deric Washburn and Steve Bochco)*—1971, Magnum Force *(with John Milius)*—1973, Thunderbolt and Lightfoot—1974, The Deer Hunter *(with Deric Washburn, Louis*

Garfinkle, and Quinn Redeker)—1978, Heavens Gate—1980

COHEN, Larry
(see also Directors)
Agent: The Sy Fischer Co.
10100 Santa Monica Blvd., Suite 2440
Los Angeles, CA 90017
Telephone: (213) 557-0388

credits: The Return of the Magnificent Seven—1970, El Condor—1970, Black Caesar—1972, It's Alive—1974, God Told Me To—1976, The Private Files of J. Edgar Hoover—1977, It Lives Again— 1978, The Ringer *(with William Richert)*— 1978, Full Moon High—1980, I, The Jury—1982

COHEN, Lawrence D.
Agent: William Morris Agency
151 El Camino Drive
Beverly Hills, CA 90212
Telephone: (213) 274-7451

credits: Carrie—1976, Ghost Story—1981

COPPOLA, Francis
(see also Directors)
Business: Zoetrope Studios
529 Pacific Street
San Francisco, CA 94133
Telephone: (415) 788-7500

credits: Patton *(with Edmund North)*— 1969, The Godfather *(with Mario Puzo)*— 1971, The Conversation—1973, The Great Gatsby—1974, The Godfather–Part II *(with Mario Puzo)*—1974, Apocalypse Now—1979, One from the Heart *(with Armyan Bernstein)*—1982, The Outsiders—1982

CRICHTON, Michael
Agent: Creative Artists Agency
1888 Century Park East, Suite 1400
Los Angeles, CA 90067
Telephone: (213) 277-4545

credits: Extreme Close-up—1973, Westworld—1973, Coma—1977, The Great

screenwriters

CRICHTON, Michael, *continued*
Train Robbery—1979; Looker—1981,
Congo—1982

CURTIN, Valerie
Agent: Creative Artists Agency
1888 Century Park East, Suite 1400
Los Angeles, CA 90067
Telephone: (213) 277-4545

credits: And Justice For All *(with Barry Levinson)*—1979, Best Friends *(with Barry Levinson)*—1982

DeFELITTA, Frank
(see also Directors Movies for TV)
Agent: Michael Marcus
Creative Artists Agency
1888 Century Park East, Suite 1400
Los Angeles, CA 90067
Telephone: (213) 277-4545

credits: Audrey Rose—1976, The Entity—1980

DeLAURENTIIS, Robert
credits: A Little Sex—1982

DeLUCA, Rudy
Agent: Creative Artists Agency
1888 Century Park East, Suite 1400
Los Angeles, CA 90067
Telephone: (213) 277-4545

credits: Silent Movie *(with Mel Brooks and Ron Clark)*—1976, High Anxiety *(with Brooks, Clark and Barry Levinson)*—1977, Caveman *(with Carl Gottlieb)*—1981

DeVORE, Christopher
Sanford-Beckett
1015 Gayley Avenue, Suite 301
Los Angeles, CA 90024
Telephone: (213) 208-2100

credits: The Elephant Man (with Eric Bergren)—1980, The Francis Farmer Story (with Eric Bergren)—[upcoming]

DeVORE, Gary
Agent: William Morris Agency
151 El Camino Drive
Beverly Hills, CA 90212
Telephone: (213) 274-7451

credits: Back Roads—1981

DIAMOND, I.A.L.
Agent: Irving Lazar
211 South Beverly Blvd., Suite 100
Beverly Hills, CA 90212
Telephone: (213) 275-6153

credits—(co-writer with Billy Wilder):
Some Like It Hot—1959, The Apartment—1960, One, Two, Three—1961, Irma La Douce—1963, The Fortune Cookie—1966, Cactus Flower *(solo):*—1969, The Front Page—1974, Fedora—1978, Buddy Buddy—1981

DICKEY, James
Agent: Raines & Raines
475 Fifth Avenue
New York, NY 10017

credits: Deliverance—1971, Klondike—1981

DOWD, Nancy
credits: Coming Home *(with Waldo Salt)*—1978

DUNNE, John Gregory
credits: True Confessions *(with Joan Didion)*—1981

ELIAS, Michael
Creative Artists
1888 Century Park East, Suite 1400
Los Angeles, CA 90067
Telephone: (213) 277-4545

credits: The Frisco Kid (with Frank Shaw)—1979, The Jerk (with Steve Martin and Carl Gottlieb)—1979, Serial—1979, Young Doctors In Love *(with Rich Eustis)*—1982

FANCHER, Hampton
(see also Producers)
Bus. Mgr.: Hersh Panitch & Co.
21243 Ventura Blvd., Suite 101
Woodland Hills, CA 91364
Telephone: (213) 999-2530
Attorney: Ken Suddleson
Telephone: (213) 552-7700
credits: Blade Runner—1982, Salvation—
[upcoming]

FEIFFER, Jules
Agent: The Lantz Office
114 East 55th Street
New York, NY 10022
Telephone: (212) 751-2107
credits: Carnal Knowledge—1971, Popeye—1980

FENADY, Andrew J.
Agent: ICM
8899 Beverly Boulevard
Los Angeles, CA 90048
Telephone: (213) 550-4000
credits: Chisum—1970, The Man with
Bogart's Face—1978

FISKIN, Jeffrey Alan
credits: Cutter's Way—1981

FOREMAN, Carl
(see also Directors)
Business: High Noon Productions
100 Universal City Plaza, Bldg. 507
Universal City, CA 91608
Telephone: (213) 508-3117
credits: Champion—1949, Home of the
Brave—1949, The Men—1950, Cyrano
de Bergerac—1951, High Noon—1952,
The Bridge on the River Kwai—1956, The
Key—1957, The Guns of Navaraone—
1961, The Victors—1964, Born
Free—1965, Mackenna's Gold—1969,
Young Winston—1972, Force 10 from
Navarone—1978, When Time Ran Out
—1979

FOSSE, Bob
(see also Directors)
Business: 850 Seventh Avenue
New York, NY 10019
Telephone: (212) 245-5049
credits: All That Jazz (with Robert Alan
Arthur)—1979

FRANK, Harriet
Agent: Ziegler, Diskant
9255 Sunset Boulevard
Los Angeles, CA 90069
Telephone: (213) 278-0070
credits: (with Irving Ravetch) Hud—1963,
Hombre—1967, The Reivers—1969, The
Cowboys—1971, Conrack—1973, Harry
Spikes—1973, Norma Rae—1978

FRIEDMAN, Bruce Jay
The Lantz Office
888 Seventh Avenue
New York, NY 10016
Telephone: (212) 586-0200
credits: Stir Crazy—1981

GALE, Bob
Agent: ICM
8899 Beverly Boulevard
Los Angeles, CA 90048
Telephone: (213) 550-4000
credits: I Want to Hold Your Hand *(with
Robert Zemeckis)*—1978, "1941" *(with
Robert Zemeckis)*—1979

GARFINKLE, Louis
Agent: Robert Stein
The Paul Kohner Agency
9169 Sunset Boulevard
Los Angeles, CA 90069
Telephone: (213) 550-1060
credits: The Deerhunter *(with Quin K.
Redeker)*—1979

GELBART, Larry
Office: c/o Writers Guild of
America—West

screenwriters

GELBART, Larry, *continued*
8955 Beverly Boulevard
Los Angeles, CA 90048
credits: Oh, God!—1977, Movie, Movie—
1978, Neighbors—1981

GILER, David
Agent: ICM
8899 Beverly Boulevard
Los Angeles, CA 90048
Telephone: (213) 550-4000
credits: Myra Breckinridge—1970, The
Parallax View *(with Lorenzo Semple, Jr.)*—
1974, The Black Bird—1975, Fun With
Dick and Jane *(with Jerry Belson and Mordecai Richler)*—1976, Southern Comfort
(with Walter Hill)—1981, The Sword *(with
Walter Hill)*—[upcoming]

GILROY, Frank
Agent: Zielger-Diskant, Inc.
9255 Sunset Boulevard
Los Angeles, CA 90069
Telephone: (213) 278-0070
credits: The Only Game in Town—1969,
Desperate Characters—1971, From
Noon Till Three—1975, Once in Paris—
1977

GODDARD, Gary
Business: Gary Goddard Productions
7033 West Sunset Boulevard
Los Angeles, CA 90046
Telephone: (213) 463-4544
credits: Tarzan—1981

GOLDMAN, Bo
Agent: William Morris Agency
151 El Camino Drive
Beverly Hills, CA 90212
Telephone: (213) 274-7451
credits: One Flew Over the Cuckoo's
Nest—1975, The Rose—1979, Melvin
and Howard—1979, Shoot the Moon—
1982, Swing Shift—1982

GOLDMAN, William
Agent: Ziegler, Diskant, Inc.
Telephone: (213) 278-0070
credits: Butch Cassidy and the Sundance
Kid—1969, The Hot Rock—1971, The
Great Waldo Pepper—1973, The Stepford
Wives—1975, All the President's Men—
1975, Marathon Man—1976, A Bridge Too
Far—1977, Magic—1978

GOODMAN, David Z.
Agent: ICM
8899 Beverly Boulevard
Los Angeles, CA 90048
Telephone: (213) 550-4000
credits: Monte Walsh—1969, Lovers and
Other Strangers—1970, Straw Dogs—
1971, Man on the Swing—1973, Farewell,
My Lovely—1975, Logan's Run—1976,
March or Die—1977, Eyes of Laura
Mars—1978

GORDON, Steve
(see also Directors)
Agent: Creative Artists Agency
1888 Century Park East, Suite 1400
Los Angeles, CA 90067
Telephone: (213) 277-4545
credits: Arthur—1981

GORE, Christopher
Agent: Fifi Oscard
New York, NY
credits: Fame—1980

GOTTLIEB, Carl
Agent: Larry Grossman & Associates
211 South Beverly Drive
Beverly Hills, CA 902112
Telephone: (213) 550-8127
credits: Jaws *(with Peter Benchley)*—
1974, Which Way Is Up? *(with Cecil
Brown)*—1977, Jaws II *(with Howard
Sackler)*—1978, The Jerk *(with Steve
Martin)*—1979, Caveman *(with Rudy
DeLuca)*—1981

GOULD, Heywood
Agent: Ziegler, Diskant
9255 Sunset Boulevard
Los Angeles, CA 90069
Telephone: (213) 278-0070
credits: Rolling Thunder (with Paul Schrader)—1976, The Boys from Brazil—1978, Fort Apache, The Bronx—1980

GRIFFITHS, Trevor
Agent: Creative Artists Agency
1888 Century Park East, Suite 1400
Los Angeles, CA 90067
Telephone: (213) 277-4545
credits: Reds (with Warren Beatty)—1981

GUARE, John
Agent: ICM
40 West 57th Street
New York, NY 10019
Telephone: (212) 556-5600
credits: Atlantic City—1981

HACKIN, Dennis
Agent: Agency for the Performing Arts
9000 Sunset Boulevard
Los Angeles, CA 90069
Telephone: (213) 273-0744

Business: Second Street Films
1137 Second Street, Suite 106
Santa Monica, CA 90403
Telephone: (213) 451-1328
credits: Wanda Nevada—1979, Bronco Billy 1980, Redwood Highway (with Neal Dobrofsky)—[upcoming]

HENRY, Buck
(see also Directors)
Agent: ICM
8899 Beverly Boulevard
Los Angeles, CA 90048
Telephone: (213) 550-4000

Business: Buck Henry/Eddie
Rissien Productions
8560 Sunset Boulevard
Los Angeles, CA 90069
Telephone: (213) 659-4080

credits: Candy—1967, The Graduate—1968, Catch-22—1969, The Owl and the Pussycat—1970, What's Up Doc? (with David Newman and Robert Benton)—1971, The Day of the Dolphin—1973, The First Family—1980

HIGGINS, Colin
(see also Directors)
Agent: Creative Artists Agency
1888 Century Park East, Suite 1400
Los Angeles, CA 90067
Telephone: (213) 277-4545
credits: Harold and Maude—1971, Silver Streak—1977, Foul Play—1978, Nine to Five (with Patricia Resnick)—1980

HILL, Walter
(see also Directors)
Office: The Phoenix Co.
2242 Cahuenga Boulevard
Hollywood, CA 90068

Agent: ICM
8899 Beverly Boulevard
Los Angeles, CA 90048
Telephone: (213) 550-4000
credits: Hickey and Boggs—1972, The Getaway—1972, The Thief Who Came to Dinner—1973, The Mackintosh Man—1973, The Drowning Pool (with Tracy Keenan Wynn and Lorenzo Semple)—1974, Hard Times (with Bruce Henstell and Bryan Gindoff)—1975, The Driver—1978, The Warriors (with David Shaber)—1979, Southern Comfort (with David Giler)—1981, The Sword (with David Giler)—[upcoming]

HOTCHNER, Tracy
Agent: Ron Mardigian
William Morris Agency
151 El Camino Drive
Beverly Hills, CA 90212
Telephone: (213) 274-7451
credits: Mommie Dearest (with Frank Yablans and Frank Perry)—1981

screenwriters

HOWARD, Ron
Office: Major H Productions
5555 Melrose Avenue
Los Angeles, CA 90038
Telephone: (213) 468-5000

credits: Grand Theft Auto *(with Rance Howard)*—1977, Leo & Loree—1979

HUYCK, Willard
Office: The Burbank Studios
4000 Warner Boulevard
Burbank, CA 91522
Telephone: (213) 954-2864

Agent: Creative Artists Agency
1888 Century Park East, Suite 1400
Los Angeles, CA 90067
Telephone: (213) 277-4545

credits (all written with Gloria Katz): American Graffiti *(with George Lucas)*—1972, Lucky Lady—1975, French Postcards—1979

HYAMS, Peter
(see also Directors)
Agent: Creative Artists Agency
1888 Century Park East, Suite 1400
Los Angeles, CA 90067
Telephone: (213) 277-4545

credits: T. R. Baskin—1971, Busting—1974, Capricorn One—1977, Telefon—1977, Hanover Street—1978, Outland—1981, Star Chamber—[not yet released]

KANE, Michael
Agent: ICM
8899 Beverly Boulevard
Los Angeles, CA 90048
Telephone: (213) 550-4000

credits: Hot Stuff—1979, Foolin' Around—1979, Hard Country—1981, The Legend of the Lone Ranger *(with Ivan Goff, William Roberts, and Ben Roberts)*—1980

KASDAN, Lawrence
(see also Directors)
Attorney: Peter Benedict
Weissman & Wolf
96091 Wilshire Boulevard
Beverly Hills, CA 90212
Telephone: (213) 858-7888

credits: The Empire Strikes Back—1979, Raiders of the Lost Ark—1981, Body Heat—1981

KATZ, Gloria
Agent: Creative Artists Agency
1888 Century Park East, Suite 1400
Los Angeles, CA 90067
Telephone: (213) 277-4545

Business: Burbank Studios
4000 Warner Boulevard
Burbank, CA 91522
Telephone: (213) 954-2864

credits (all written with Willard Huyck): American Graffiti *(with George Lucas)*—1972, Lucky Lady—1975, French Postcards—1979

KAUFMAN, Philip
(see also Directors)
Agent: Creative Artists Agency
1888 Century Park East, Suite 1400
Los Angeles, CA 90067
Telephone: (213) 277-4545

credits: Fearless Frank—1969, The Great Northfield, Minnesota Raid—1971, The White Dawn—1974, Outlaw—Josey Wales—1976, Invasion of the Body Snatchers—1978, The Wanderers—1979, The Right Stuff—1983

KAUFMAN, Robert
Agent: Creative Artists Agency
1888 Century Park East, Suite 1400
Los Angeles, CA 90067
Telephone: (213) 277-4545

credits: Getting Straight—1969, I Love My Wife—1970, Freebie and the Bean—1973, Harry and Walter Go to New

KUFMAN, Robert, *continued*
York—1976, The Happy Hooker Goes to
Washington—1977, Love at First Bite
with Mark Gindes)—1979, Nothing Personal—1979

KERBY, Bill
Agent: Adams, Ray & Rosenberg
9200 Sunset Boulevard
Los Angeles, CA 90069
Telephone: (213) 278-3000
credits: The Dion Brothers—1974, Hooper
(with Thomas Rickman)—1978, Firepower
(with Michael Winner)—1978, The Rose
(with Bo Goldman)—1979

KOSINSKI, Jerzy
c/o Scientia-Factum, Inc.
Hemisphere House
60 West 57th Street
New York, NY 10019
credits: Being There—1979, Passion
Play—1982

KRONSBERG, Jeremy Joe
Agent: The Ufland Agency
190 North Canon Drive, Suite 202
Beverly Hills, CA 90210
Telephone: (213) 273-9441
credits: Every Which Way But Loose—
1978

KUBRICK, Stanley
(see also Directors)
Attorney: Louis C. Blau, Beverly Hills
Telephone: (213) 552-7774
credits: A Clockwork Orange—1971,
Barry Lyndon—1975, The Shining—1979

LAURENTS, Arthur
Paramus Artists Associates
1414 Avenue of the Americas
New York, NY 10019
credits: Rope—1948, West Side Story—
1960, The Way We Were—1973, The
Turning Point—1977

LEHMAN, Ernest
Agent: William Morris Agency
151 El Camino Drive
Beverly Hills, CA 90212
Telephone: (213) 274-7451
credits: Executive Suite—1954, Sabrina—1954, The King and I—1956, Somebody Up There Likes Me—1956, Sweet
Smell of Success—1957, North by Northwest—1959, From the Terrace—1960,
West Side Story—1960, The Prize—1963,
The Sound of Music—1964, Who's Afraid
of Virginia Woolf—1967, Hello Dolly—
1969, Portnoy's Complaint—1971, Family
Plot—1975, Black Sunday—1976

LEONE, John
Agent: William Morris Agency
151 El Camino Drive
Beverly Hills, CA 90212
Telephone: (213) 274-7451
credits: The Last of the Cowboys—1977,
Tough Dreams—1981

LEVINSON, Barry
Agent: Creative Artists Agency
1888 Century Park East, Suite 1400
Los Angeles, CA 90067
Telephone: (213) 277-4545
credits: Silent Movie *(with Mel Brooks)*—
1976, High Anxiety *(with Mel Brooks &
Rudy Deluca)*—1977, And Justice For All
(with Valerie Curtin)—1979, Diner—1981,
Best Friends *(with Valerie Curtin)*—1982

LIVINGSTON, Harold
Contact: Writers Guild West
8955 Beverly Boulevard
Los Angeles, CA 90048
Telephone: (213) 550-1000
credits: Star Trek—The Motion Picture—
1979

screenwriters

LUEDTKE, Kurt
Agent: Zieglar, Diskant
9255 Sunset Boulevard
Los Angeles, CA 90069
Telephone: (213) 278-0070
credits: Absence of Malice—1981

MALICK, Terrence
(see also Directors)
Agent: Ziegler, Diskant
9255 Sunset Boulevard
Los Angeles, CA 90069
Telephone: (213) 278-0070
credits: Deadhead Miles—1971, Pocket Money—1972, Badlands—1973, Days of Heaven—1978

MAMET, David
c/o Howard Rosenstone
3 East 48th Street
New York, NY 10017

MANKIEWICZ, Tom
Agent: ICM
8899 Beverly Boulevard
Los Angeles, CA 90048
Telephone: (213) 550-4000
credits: Live and Let Die—1973, The Man with the Golden Gun—1974, Mother, Jugs and Speed—1976, The Eagle Has Landed *(with Jack Higgens)*—1977, The Cassandra Crossing *(with Robert Kate and George Cosmatos)*—1977

MANN, Michael
(see also Directors)
Agent: Jeff Berg, ICM
8899 Beverly Boulevard
Los Angeles, CA 90048
Telephone: (213) 550-4000
credits: Thief—1981

MARCUS, Lawrence B.
Agent: ICM
8899 Beverly Boulevard
Los Angeles, CA 90048
Telephone: (213) 550-4000

credits: Witness for the Prosecution—1957, Petulia—1968, Justine—1969, The Stunt Man—1980

MARVIN, Mike
credits: Six Pack *(with Alex Matter)*—1982

MATHESON, Richard
Agent: Adams, Ray & Rosenberg
9200 Sunset Boulevard, Penthouse 25
Los Angeles, CA 90069
Telephone: (213) 278-3000
credits: De Sade—1969, The Omega Man—1972, The Legend of Hell House—1973, Somewhere in Time—1979

MAY, Elaine
c/o Wien, Sales, & Vizvary
8909 West Olympic Blvd, Suite 200
Beverly Hills, CA 90211
credits: A New Leaf—1970, Such Good Friends—1971, Mickey and Nicky—1975, Heaven Can Wait—1978

MAYES, Wendell
Agent: Ziegler, Diskant
9255 Sunset Boulevard
Los Angeles, CA 90069
Telephone: (213) 278-0070
credits: The Poseidon Adventure *(with Stirling Silliphant)*—1972, The Revengers—1972, The Bank Shot—1974, Death Wish—1974, Go Tell the Spartans—1978, Love and Bullets, Charlie—1978

MAZURSKY, Paul
(see also Directors)
Agent: ICM
8899 Beverly Boulevard
Los Angeles, CA 90048
Telephone: (213) 550-4000
credits: Bob and Carol and Ted and Alice—1969, Alex in Wonderland *(with Larry Tucker)*—1970, Blume in Love—1972, Next Stop Greenwich Village—1975, An Unmarried Woman—1977, Willie & Phil—1979

MERRILL, Kieth
(see also Directors)

MEYER, Nicholas
(see also Directors)
    Contact: International Business Mgmt.
    1801 Century Park East
    Los Angeles, CA 90067

credits: The Seven Percent Solution—1976, Time After Time—1978

MEYERS, Nancy
    Agent: ICM
    8899 Beverly Boulevard
    Los Angeles, CA 90048
    Telephone: (213) 550-4000

credits: Private Benjamin *(with Charles Shyer and Harvey Miller)*—1980

MILIUS, John
(see also Directors)
    Agent: ICM
    8899 Beverly Boulevard
    Los Angeles, CA 90048
    Telephone: (213) 550-4000

credits: Evel Knievel *(with Alan Caillow)*—1971, Jeremiah Johnson *(with Edward Anhalt)*—1971, The Life and Times of Judge Roy Bean—1972, Dillinger—1972, Magnum Force *(with Michael Cimino)*—1973, The Wind and the Lion—1975, Big Wednesday *(with Dennis Aaberg)*—1977, Apocalypse Now *(with Francis Coppola)*—1979, Conan the Barbarian—1982

NEWMAN, David
    Agent: ICM
    40 West 57th Street
    New York, NY 10019
    Telephone: (212) 556-5600

credits: Bonnie and Clyde—1967, Superman—1978, Superman II *(with Leslie Newman)*—1981, Tough Enough *(with Frank Gilroy)*—1982

NICIPHOR, Nicholas
    Agent: ICM
    8899 Beverly Boulevard
    Los Angeles, CA 90048
    Telephone: (213) 550-4000

credits: Our Winning Season—1978

NORTH, Edmund H.
    Eisenbach–Greene–Duchow
    760 North La Cienega Boulevard
    Los Angeles, CA 90069
    Telephone: (213) 659-3420

credits: Patton *(with Francis Coppola)*—1969, Meteor *(with Stanley Mann)*—1977

NORTON, Bill, Sr.
    Agent: Irv Schechter Co.
    404 North Roxbury Drive, Suite 800
    Beverly Hills, CA 90210
    Telephone: (213) 278-8070

credits: Dirty Tricks, Night of the Juggler, Day of the Animals, Moving Violation, Big Bad Mama, Sam Whiskey—1969, The Hunting Party—1971, Trader Horn—1973, White Lightning—1973, Brannigan—1975, A Small Town in Texas—1976, Gator—1976

O'BANNON, Dan
    Agent: Cosay, Werner & Associates
    9744 Wilshire Boulevard
    Beverly Hills, CA 90212
    Telephone: (213) 550-1535

credits: Dark Star—1973, Alien—1979, Heavy Metal—1981, Dead and Buried—1982, Blue Thunder—1982

ORMSBY, Alan
    Agent: Sanford-Beckett Agency
    1015 Gayley Avenue, Suite 301
    Los Angeles, CA 90024
    Telephone: (213) 208-2100

credits: My Bodyguard—1979, The Little Dragons—1979

PALLENBERG, Rospo
Agent: Agency for the Performing Arts
9000 Sunset Boulevard
Los Angeles, CA 90069
Telephone: (213) 273-0744

credits: Excalibur *(with John Boorman)*—1981

PARENT, Gail
Agent: Creative Artists Agency
1888 Century Park East, Suite 1400
Los Angeles, CA 90067
Telephone: (213) 277-4545

credits: Sheila Levine—1974, The Main Event *(with Andrew Smith)*—1979

PERRY, Frank
(see also Directors)
Business: Frank Perry Films
655 Park Avenue
New York, NY 10021

credits: Mommie Dearest *(with Tracy Hotchner and Frank Yablans)*—1981, Nightwork—1982

PIERSON, Frank
Agent: Adams, Ray & Rosenberg
9200 Sunset Boulevard
Los Angeles, CA 90046
Telephone: (213) 278-3000

credits: Cool Hand Luke—1967, The Happening—1967, Cat Ballou *(with Walter Newman)*—1967, The Looking Glass War—1969, The Anderson Tapes—1971, Dog Day Afternoon—1975, A Star Is Born *(with John Gregory Dunne and Joan Didion)*—1976, King of the Gypsies—1979

PINTER, Harold
Agent: Jimmy Wax
16 Cadogan Lane
London, S.W. 1 England

credits: The French Lieutenant's Woman—1981, Betrayal—1982

PLATT, Polly
Agent: Adams, Ray & Rosenberg
9200 Sunset Boulevard
Los Angeles, CA 90046
Telephone: (213) 278-3000

credits: Pretty Baby—1977, Good Luck, Miss Wyckoff—1978

PONICSAN, Darryl
c/o Ned Brown
407 North Maple Drive
Beverly Hills, CA 90210

credits: Cinderella Liberty—1973, The Last Detail—1974, Taps—1981

POPE, Tom
Agent: Robert Stein
      The Paul Kohner Agency
9169 Sunset Boulevard
Los Angeles, CA 90069
Telephone: (213) 550-1060

credits: Winning—1969, The Manitou—1978, Hammett—1980, The Lords of Discipline *(with Lloyd Fonvielle)*—1982

PUZO, Mario
Attorney: Bert Fields
Los Angeles, CA
Telephone: (213) 272-8252

credits: The Godfather *(with Francis Coppola)*—1971, The Godfather–Part II *(with Francis Coppola)*—1974, Superman *(with David Newman, Leslie Newman, Robert Benton)*—1978

RAMIS, Harold
(see also Directors)
Agent: Creative Artists Agency
1888 Century Park East, Suite 1400
Los Angeles, CA 90067
Telephone: (213) 277-4545

credits: National Lampoon's Animal House *(with Douglas Kenney and Chris Miller)*—1978, Meatballs *(with Len Blum*

RAMIS, Harold, *continued*
and Dan Goldberg)—1979, The Caddy-shack *(with Brian Doylc Murray and Douglas Kenny)*—1980, Stripes *(with Blum and Goldberg)*—1981

RASCOE, Judith
Agent: William Morris Agency
151 El Camino Drive
Beverly Hills, CA 90212
Telephone: (213) 274-7451

credits: Who'll Stop the Rain *(with Robert Stone)*—1977, A Portrait of the Artist as a Young Man—1979, Endless Love—1981

RAUCHER, Herman
Business Manager: Arthur Green
Los Angeles, CA 900??
Telephone: (213) 246-1900

credits: Sweet November—1968, Watermelon Man—1969, Summer of '42—1971, Class of '44—1973, Ode to Billie Joe—1976, The Other Side of Midnight—1977

RAVETCH, Irving
Agent: Ziegler, Diskant
9255 Sunset Boulevard
Los Angeles, CA 90069
Telephone: (213) 278-0070

credits (all written with Harriet Frank):
Hud—1963, Hombre—1967, The Reivers—1969, The Cowboys—1971, Conrack—1973, Harry Spikes—1973, Norma Rae—1978

RESNICK, Patricia
Agent: William Morris Agency
151 El Camino Drive
Beverly Hills, CA 90212
Telephone: (213) 274-7451

credits: A Wedding—1978, 9 to 5—1981

RICHERT, William
Agent: William Morris Agency
151 El Camino Drive
Beverly Hills, CA 90212
Telephone: (213) 274-7451

credits: The Ringer—1978, Winter Kills—1979

RICHTER, W. D.
Agent: Shapiro-Lichtman, Inc.
2049 Century Park East
Los Angeles, CA 90067
Telephone: (213) 557-2244

credits: Slither—1972, Fat Chance—1974, Nickelodeon—1976, The Invasion of the Body Snatchers—1978, Dracula—1979, Brubaker *(with Arthur Ross)*—1979, The Ninja—1981, All Night Long—1981

RICKMAN, Thomas
Agent: Creative Artists Agency
1888 Century Park East, Suite 1400
Los Angeles, CA 90067
Telephone: (213) 277-4545

credits: Kansas City Bomber—1972, The Laughing Policeman—1973, The White Dawn—1974, W. W. and the Dixie Dance Kings—Hooper—1978, Coal Miner's Daughter—1980

ROBERTS, William
c/o Sy Fischer Company
10100 Santa Monica Blvd., Suite 2440
Los Angeles, CA 90067

credits: The Bridge at Remagen—1969, Red Sun *(with Denne Petitclerc and Lawrence Roman)*—1971, The Last American Hero—1973, Posse—1975, The Legend of the Lone Ranger *(with Ivan Goff, Michael Kane and Ben Roberts)*—1980

ROSENBERG, Jeanne
credits: The Black Stallion *(with William Wittliff and Melissa Matheson)*—1979

SALT, Waldo
Agent: Creative Artists Agency
1888 Century Park East, Suite 1400
Los Angeles, CA 90067
Telephone: (213) 277-4545

credits: The Shop Worn Angel, Rachel and the Stranger, Flame and the Arrow, Midnight Cowboy—1969, The Gang That Couldn't Shoot Straight—1971, Serpico—

SALT, Waldo, *continued*
1973, The Day of the Locust—1974, Coming Home—1977,

SANDLER, Barry
Agent: William Morris Agency
151 El Camino Drive
Beverly Hills, CA 90212
Telephone: (213) 274-7451

credits: Julio and Stein—1971, The Loners *(with John Lawrence)*—1971, Kansas City Bomber—1972, The Duchess and the Dirtwater Fox *(with Melvin Frank & Jack Rose)*—1975, Gable and Lombard—1976, The Mirror Crack'd—1980, Making Love *(with Scott Berg)*—1982

SARGENT, Alvin
Agent: Adams, Ray & Rosenberg
9200 Sunset Boulevard, Penthouse 25
Los Angeles, CA 90046
Telephone: (213) 278-3000

credits: The Sterile Cuckoo—1969, I Walk the Line—1969, Paper Moon—1972, Love and Pain and the Whole Damn Thing—1973, Bobby Deerfield—1976, Julia—1977, Straight Time—1977, Ordinary People—1980

SAYLES, John
Agent: Robinson-Weintraub Assoc.
554 South San Vicente Blvd.
Los Angeles, CA 90048
Telephone: (213) 653-5802

credits: Piranha—1978, The Lady in Red—1979, Return of the Secaucus Seven—1980, The Howling—1980, Battle Beyond the Stars—1980, The Challenge—1982

SCHMOELLER, David
(see also Directors)
Business: The Schmoeller Corp.
2244 Stanley Hills Drive
Los Angeles, CA 90046
Telephone: (213) 654-0748

credits: Tourist Trap *(with Larry Carroll)*—1978, The Day Time Ended—1980, The Seduction—1982

SCHNEIDER, Barry
Agent: Lew Weitzman
9171 Wilshire Boulevard
Beverly Hills, CA 902112
Telephone: (213) 278-5562

credits: Blood Ruby—1976, Harper Valley PTA—1978, Roller Boogie—1979, Take This Job And Shove It—1980

SCHRADER, Paul
(see also Directors)
Agent: ICM
8899 Beverly Boulevard
Los Angeles, CA 90048
Telephone: (213) 550-4000

credits: The Yakuza *(with Robert Towne)*—1974, Taxi Driver—1976, Obsession—1976, Rolling Thunder *(with Heywood Gould)*—1977, Blue Collar *(with Leonard Schrader)*—1978, Hard Core—1978, American Gigolo—1979

SEMPLE, Lorenzo, Jr.
Agent: Creative Artists Agency
1888 Century Park East, Suite 1400
Los Angeles, CA 90067
Telephone: (213) 277-4545

credits: The Sporting Club—1970, The Marriage of a Young Stockbroker—1971, Super Cops—1973, Papillon *(with Dalton Trumbo)*—1973, The Paralax View *(with David Giler)*—1974, The Drowning Pool *(with Tracy Keenan Wynn and Walter Hill)*—1975, Three Days of the Condor *(with David Rayfiel)*—1975, King Kong-1976, Hurricane—1978

SHABER, David
Contact: Writers Guild of America,
    East
555 West 57th Street
New York, NY 10019

SHABER, David, *continued*

credits: Last Embrace—1978, The Warriors *(with Walter Hill)*—1978, Those Lips, Those Eyes—1980, Nighthawks—1981, Rollover—1982

SHAGAN, Steve
Agent: Creative Artists Agency
1888 Century Park East, Suite 1400
Los Angeles, CA 90067
Telephone: (213) 277-4545

credits: Save the Tiger—1973, Hustle—1975, The Voyage—1976, Nightwing *(with Edwin Shake and Martin Smith)*—1978, The Formula—1980

SHUSETT, Ronald

credits: Alien *(with Dan O'Bannon)*—1979, Dead and Buried *(with Dan O'Bannon)*—1981

SHYER, Charles
Agent: ICM
8899 Beverly Boulevard
Los Angeles, CA 90048
Telephone: (213) 550-4000

credits: Smokey and the Bandit *(with Alan Mandel and James Barrett)*—1977, Goin' South *(Alan Mandel, John Shaner, and Al Ramus)*—1977, House Calls *(with Mandel, Max Shulman, and Julius Epstein)*—1977, Private Benjamin—1980

SILLIPHANT, Stirling
(see also Producers, Movies for TV)
Manager: Don Kopaloff
Agent: Creative Artists Agency
1888 Century Park East, Suite 1400
Los Angeles, CA 90067
Telephone: (213) 277-4545

credits: In the Heat of the Night—1967, Charly—1968, Marlowe—1969, A Walk in the Spring Rain—1969, The Liberation of L.B. Jones—1970, Murphy's War—1971, The New Centurions—1972, The Poseidon Adventure—1972, Shaft in Africa—1973, The Towering Inferno—1974, The Killer Elite—1975, The Enforcer—1976, Telefon—1977, The Swarm—1977, Circle of Iron—1978, When Time Ran Out—1979

SIMON, Neil
Contact: Writers Guild of America, West
8955 Beverly Boulevard
Los Angeles, CA 90048
Telephone: (213) 550-1000

credits: The Out-of-Towners—1969, Plaza Suite—1970, Last of the Red Hot Lovers—1971, The Heartbreak Kid—1972, The Prisoner of Second Avenue—1974, The Sunshine Boys—1975, Murder by Death—1975, The Goodbye Girl—1977, The Cheap Detective—1977, California Suite 1978, Chapter Two—1979, Seems Like Old Times—1980, Only When I Laugh—1981, I Ought to Be in Pictures—1982

SLADE, Bernard
Agent: Major Talent Agency, Inc.
11812 San Vicente Blvd, Suite 510
Los Angeles, CA 90049
Telephone: (213) 820-5841

credits: Stand Up and Be Counted—1971, Same Time Next Year—1979, Tribute—1980

SOBIESKI, Carol
Agent: Adams, Ray & Rosenberg
9200 Sunset Blvd., Pent. 25
Los Angeles, CA 90069
Telephone: (213) 278-3000

credits: Annie—1982, The Toy—1982

STALLONE, Sylvester
(see also Directors)
Agent: Creative Artists Agency
1888 Century Park East, Suite 1400
Los Angeles, CA 90067
Telephone: (213) 277-4545

STALLONE, Sylvester, *continued*
credits: Rocky—1976, F.I.S.T. *(with Joe Eszterhas)*—1977, Paradise Alley—1978, Rocky II—1979, Rocky III—1982, First Blood *(with Michael Kozoll)*—1983

STEINBERG, Norman
Office: MGM Studios
10202 Washington Blvd.
Culver City, CA 90230
Telephone: (213) 558-5435

credits: Blazing Saddles *(with Andrew Bergman, Richard Pryor, and Mel Brooks)*—1973, My Favorite Year—1981, Yes, Giorgio—1981

STEWART, Douglas Day
Agent: William Morris Agency
151 El Camino Drive
Beverly Hills, CA 90212
Telephone: (213) 274-7451

credits: The Blue Lagoon—1980, An Officer and a Gentleman—1982

STONE, Oliver
(see also Directors)
Business: Ixtlan, Inc.
9025 Wilshire Blvd.
Beverly Hills, CA 90211
Telephone: (213) 858-1276

credits: Seizure—1974, Midnight Express—1978, The Hand—1981, Conan the Barbarian *(co-writer with John Milius)*—1982

STONE, Peter
Agent: William Morris Agency
151 El Camino Drive
Beverly Hills, CA 90212
Telephone: (213) 274-7451

credits: Charade—1963, Father Goose—1964, Mirage—1965, The Secret World of Harry Frigg—1967, Sweet Charity—1968, The Skin Game—1971, "1776"—1972, The Taking of Pelham 1-2-3—1974, Silver Bears—1977, Who Is Killing the Great Chefs of Europe?—1978

TESICH, Steve
Agent: ICM
8899 Beverly Boulevard
Los Angeles, CA 90048
Telephone: (213) 550-4000

credits: Breaking Away—1979, Eyewitness—1981, Four Friends—1981, The World According to Garp—1982

TEWKESBURY, Joan
Agent: ICM
8899 Beverly Boulevard
Los Angeles, CA 90048
Telephone: (213) 550-4000

credits: Thieves Like Us *(with Calder Willingham and Robert Altman)*—1973, Nashville—1974, Ladies Night—1981

THOMPSON, Ernest
Agent: William Morris Agency
151 El Camino Drive
Beverly Hills, CA 90212
Telephone: (213) 274-7451

credits: On Golden Pond—1981 *(Academy Award, Best Screenplay Adaptation—1981)*

TIDYMAN, Ernest
Agent: ICM
8899 Beverly Boulevard
Los Angeles, CA 90048
Telephone: (213) 550-4000

credits: The French Connection—1971, Shaft—1971, Shaft's Big Score—1972, High Plains Drifter—1972, Report to the Commissioner *(with Abby Mann)*—1974, Street People—1976, A Force of One—1979

TOWNE, Robert
Agent: Creative Artists Agency
1888 Century Park East, Suite 1400
Los Angeles, CA 90067
Telephone: (213) 277-4545

credits: The Last Detail—1973, Chinatown—1974, Shampoo *(with Warren Beatty)*—1974, Personal Best—1981

VERNONA, Steve
(see also Directors)
Agent: ICM
8899 Beverly Boulevard
Los Angeles, CA 90048
Telephone: (213) 550-4000

credits: The Lords of Flatbush—1974,
Pipe Dreams—1976, Boardwalk *(with
Leigh Chapman)*—1979

WARD, David S.
Agent: ICM
8899 Beverly Boulevard
Los Angeles, CA 90048
Telephone: (213) 550-4000

credits: Steelyard Blues—1972, The
Sting—1973, Cannery Row—1981, The
Next Sting—1982

WELLAND, Colin
c/o Enigma Overseas Variations
The Burbank Studios
4000 Warner Boulevard
Burbank, CA 91522
Telephone: (213) 954-3673

Agent: Creative Artists Agency
1888 Century Park East, Suite 1400
Los Angeles, CA 90067
Telephone: (213) 277-4545

credits: Chariots of Fire *(Academy Award,
Best Original Screenplay—1981)*

WELLER, Michael
Agent: Howard Rosenstone
3 East 48th Street
New York, NY 10017
credits: Ragtime—1981

WEXLER, Norman
Agent: Marvin Moss, Inc.
9200 Sunset Boulevard, Suite 601
Los Angeles, CA 90069
Telephone: (213) 274-8483

credits: Joe—1970, Serpico *(with Waldo
Salt)*—1973, Mandingo—1975, Saturday
Night Fever—1977

WILDER, Gene
Pal-Mel Productions
9350 Wilshire Blvd., Suite 400
Beverly Hills, CA 90212

credits: Young Frankenstein *(with Mel
Brooks)*—1974, The Adventures of Sherlock Holmes' Smarter Brother—1975
(and Directed)

WINNER, Michael
(see also Directors)
Agent: Chasin-Park-Citron
9255 Sunset Boulevard, Suite 910
Los Angeles, CA 90069
Telephone: (213) 273-7190

credits: The Sentinel—1976, Firepower—
1978, Death Wish II *(with David Engel-
bach)*—1981

WITTLIFF, William
Agent: ICM
8899 Beverly Boulevard
Los Angeles, CA 90048
Telephone: (213) 550-4000

credits: The Black Stallion *(with Melissa
Matheson and Jeanne Rosenberg)*—
1979, Raggedy Man—1981

WYNN, Tracy Keenan
Contact: Writers Guild West
8955 Beverly Boulevard
Los Angeles, CA 90048
Telephone: (213) 550-1000

credits: The Longest Yard—1973, The
Drowning Pool *(with Lorenzo Semple, Jr.
and Walter Hill)*—1975, The Deep (with
Peter Benchley)—1977

YABLANS, Frank
Business: Frank Yablans Productions
10201 West Pico Blvd.
Los Angeles, CA 90035
Telephone: (213) 203-1334

credits: North Dallas Forty *(with Ted
Kotcheff and Peter Gent)*—1979, Mom-
mie Dearest *(with Frank Perry and Tracy
Hotchner)*—1981

YOUNG, Darlene
c/o Lorimar Productions
3970 Overland Avenue
Culver City, CA 90230

credits: Little Darlings—1980, Cross Creek—1982

ZEMECKIS, Robert
(see also Directors)
Agent: ICM
8899 Beverly Boulevard
Los Angeles, CA 90048
Telephone: (213) 550-4000

credits (all co-written with Bob Gale): I Want to Hold Your Hand—1978, "1941"—1979, Used Cars—1980

ZUCKER, David and Jerry
(see also Directors)
Office: Paramount Pictures
5451 Marathon Street
Los Angeles, CA 90038
Telephone: (213) 468-5000

credits: (with Jim Abrahams) Kentucky Fried Movie—1977, Airplane—1980

CINEMATOGRAPHERS

cinematographers

ALMENDROS, Nestor, A.S.C.
Agent: Smith/Gosnell Agency
20154 Pacific Coast Highway
Malibu, CA 90265
Telephone: (213) 456-6641

credits: Goin' South—1978, Days of Heaven *(academy award, best cinematography)*—1978, The Blue Lagoon—1980, Stab—1982, Sophie's Choice—1983

ALONZO, John, A.S.C.
Agent: Chasin-Park-Citron
9255 Sunset Blvd., Suite 910
Los Angeles, CA 90069
Telephone: (213) 273-7190

credits: Bloody Mama—1970, Harold and Maude—1971, Vanishing Point—1971, Get to Know Your Rabbit—1972, Sounder—1972, Pete 'n' Tillie—1972, Lady Sings the Blues—1972, Chinatown—1974, Conrack—1974, Farewell My Lovely—1975, The Fortune—1975, Once Is Not Enough—1975, The Bad News Bears—1976, I Will, I Will . . . For Now—1976, Which Way Is Up?—1977, Black Sunday—1977, Sgt. Peppers Lonely Hearts Club Band—1978, Close Encounters of the Third Kind—1978, Casey's Shadow—1978, The Cheap Detective—Tom Horn—1980, Back Roads—1981, Zorro, the Gay Blade—1981, Cross Creek—1982

BIROC, Joseph, A.S.C.
Agent: Mark Lichtman
Telephone: (213) 652-9825

credits: Bye Bye Birdie—1963, The Russians Are Coming, the Russians Are Coming—1966, The Detective—1968, Too Late the Hero—1969, Mrs. Pollifax-Spy—1970, The Grissom Gang—1971, Ulzana's Raid—1972, Cahill, U.S. Marshall—1973, Blazing Saddles—1974, The Longest

Yard—1974, The Towering Inferno—1974, Hustle—1975, The Duchess and the Dirtwater Fox—1976, The Choir Boys—1977

BODE, Ralf, A.S.C.
Agent: Smith/Gosnell Agency
20154 Pacific Coast Highway
Malibu, CA 90265
Telephone: (213) 456-6641

credits: Saturday Night Fever—1977, Rich Kids—1979, Coal Miner's Daughter—1980, A Little Sex—1982

BUTLER, Wilmer, A.S.C.
Agent: Crayton Smith
Smith/Gosnell Agency
20154 Pacific Coast Highway
Malibu, CA 90265
Telephone: (213) 456-6641

credits: Hickey and Boggs—1972, The Conversation—1974, Jaws—1975, One Flew Over the Cuckoos Nest—1975, Alex and the Gypsy—1976, The Bingo Long Traveling All Stars—1976, Lipstick—1976, Demon Seed—1977, Capricorn One—1978, Rocky II—1979, Can't Stop the Music—1979, Stripes—1981

CHAPMAN, Michael
credits: The Last Detail—1973, White Dawn—1973, The Front—1976, Taxi Driver—1976, Fingers—1978, The Last Waltz—1978, Raging Bull—1980, Dead Men Don't Wear Plaid—1982

COOPERMAN, Jack
credits: Raise the Titanic—1980, Cannery Row—1981, The Challenge—1982

CORRELL, Charles
credits: Waling Tall, Part III, National Lampoon's Animal House—1978, Fast Break—1979

CRABE, James, A.S.C.
Agent: Mortie Gutterman
190 N. Canon Drive
Beverly Hills, CA 90210

credits: ZigZag—1970, Save the Tiger—1972, W.W. and the Dixie Dancekings—1975, Rocky—1976, The China Syndrome—1979, Players—1979, How to Beat the High Cost of Living—1980, The Formula—1980

CRONENWEITH, Jordon
credits: Altered States—1981, Best Friends—1982

DESCHANEL, Caleb
Office: Zoetrope Studios
1040 North Las Palmas Blvd.
Los Angeles, CA 90038
Telephone: (213) 463-7191

credits: The Black Stallion—1979

FRAKER, William, A.S.C.
(see also Directors)
Agent: Phil Gersh Agency
222 North Canon Drive, Suite 201
Beverly Hills, CA 90210
Telephone: (213) 274-6611

credits: The President's Analyst—1967, Games—1967, The Fox—1968, Bullitt—1968, Rosemary's Baby—1968, Paint Your Wagon—1969, Dusty and Sweets McGee—1971, The Day of the Dolphin—1973, Rancho De Lixe—1974, Aloha Bobby and Rose—1975, One Flew Over The Cuckoo's Nest—1975, Looking For Mr. Goodbar—1977, Close Encounters of the Third Kind—1977, American Hot Wax—1978, Heaven Can Wait—1978, "1941"—1979, Sharky's Machine—1981

HALL, Conrad, A.S.C.
Agent: ICM
8899 Beverly Boulevard
Los Angeles, CA 90048
Telephone: (213) 550-4000

credits: Harper—1965, The Professionals—1966, Cool Hand Luke—1967, In Cold Blood—1967, Butch Cassidy and the Sundance Kid *(academy award, best cinematography)*—1969, Tell Them Willie Boy is Here—1969, Fat City—1972, Electra Glide in Blue—1973, Smile—1975, The Day of the Locust—1975

KEMPER, Victor, A.S.C.
Agent: Phil Gersh Agency
222 North Canon Drive, Suite 201
Beverly Hills, CA 90210
Telephone: (213) 274-6611

credits: Husbands—1970, Who Is Harry Kellerman?—1971, They Might Be Giants—1971, The Hospital—1971, The Last of the Red Hot Lovers—1972, The Candidate—1972, Shamus—1972, Gordon's War—1973, The Friends of Eddie Coyle, The Reincarnation of Peter Proud—1974, Dog Day Afternoon—1975, The Gambler—1975, Mikey and Nicky—1976, The Last Tycoon—1976, Slap Shot—1977, Audrey Rose—1977, Coma—1978, And Justice For All—1979, Night of the Juggler—1980, Partners—1982

KOENEKAMP, Fred J., A.S.C.
Agent: Mortie Gutterman
190 North Canon Drive
Beverly Hills, CA 90210
Telephone: (213) 652-3961

credits: Patton—1970, The Great Bank Robbery, Beyond the Valley of the Dolls—1970, Billy Jack—1971, The Magnificent Seven Ride—1972, Rage—1972, Kansas City Bomber—1972, Papillon—1973, Harry in Your Pocket—1973, The Domino Principle—1973, The Towering Inferno—1974, Fun with Dick and Jane—1977,

KOENEKAMP, Fred, *continued*

Islands in the Stream—1978, The Other Side of Midnight—1978, The Champ—1979, The Amityville Horror—1979, The Hunter—1980

KOVACS, Laszlo, A.S.C.
Agent: Nicholson/Landers
13791 Riverside Drive, Suite 314
Sherman Oaks, CA 91423
Telephone: (213) 906-2700

credits: Hell's Angels on Wheels—1967, Targets—1968, Easy Rider—1969, That Cold Day in the Park—1969, Getting Straight—1970, Five Easy Pieces—1970, Alex in Wonderland—1970, The King of Marvin Gardens—1972, Pocket Money—1972, What's Up, Doc?—1972, Paper Moon—1973, Huckleberry Finn—1974, For Pete's Sake—1974, Freebie and the Bean—1974, Shampoo—1975, Baby Blue Marine—1976, Harry and Walter Go To New York—1976, New York, New York—1977, F.I.S.T.—1978, The Last Waltz—1978, Paradise Alley—1978, Butch and Sundance: The Early Days—1979, The Runner Stumbles—1979, Heart Beat—1980, Inside Moves—1980, The Legend of the Lone Ranger—1981, The Toy—1982

LASZLO, Andrew, A.S.C.
Contact: American Society of
Cinematographers
1782 North Orange Drive
Hollywood, CA 90028
Telephone: (213) 876-5080

credits: The Out of Towners—1970, The Owl and the Pussycat—1970, Lovers and Other Strangers—1970, Jennifer on My Mine—1971, Countdown at Kusini—1976, Thieves—1977, Somebody Killed Her Husband—1978, The Warriors—1978, Shogun *(television)*—1980

LATHROP, Philip, A.S.C.
Agent: Mortie Gutterman
190 North Canon Drive, Suite 202
Beverly Hills, CA 90210
Telephone: (213) 652-3961

credits: Days of Wine and Roses—1963, Girl Happy—1965, Never Too Late—1965, The Cincinnati Kid—1965, Point Blank—1967, They Shoot Horses, Don't They?—1969, The Gypsy Moths—1969, The Hawaiians—1970, The Wild Rovers—1971, The Thief Who Came To Dinner—1972, Mame—1974, Swashbuckler—1976, Airport '77—1977, The Driver—1977, Moment by Moment—1978, Little Miss Marker—1979, A Change of Seasons—1980, All Night Long—1980

MANKOFSKY, Isidor, A.S.C.
Agent: Grace Lyons
Telephone: (213) 652-5290

credits: The Muppet Movie—1979, Somewhere in Time—1980, The Jazz Singer—1980

NYKVIST, Sven, A.S.C.
Agent: Milton Forman
Telephone: (213) 274-6086

credits: The Serpent's Egg—1976, Face to Face—1976, King of the Gypsies—1977, Starting Over—1978, Pretty Baby—1979, Willie and Phil—1979, Hurricane—1979, The Postman Always Rings Twice—1980

PHILLIPS, Frank, A.S.C.
Agent: Tommy Miller
Telephone: (213) 849-2363

credits: Bedknobs and Broomsticks—1971, World's Greatest Athlete—1973, The Apple Dumpling Gang Rides Again—1979

ROIZMAN, Owen, A.S.C.
Agent: Murray Neidorf
Telephone: (213) 553-0171
credits: The Gang That Couldn't Shoot Straight—1971, The French Connection—1971, Play It Again, Sam—1972, The Heartbreak Kid—1973, The Exorcist—1974, The Taking of Pelham 1-2-3, The Stepford Wives—1974, Three Days of the Condor—1975, Network—1977, Straight Time—1978, The Electric Horseman—1979, The Black Marble—1980, True Confessions—1981, Tootsie—1982

SOUTH, Leonard, A.S.C.
Contact: The American Society of Cinematographers
1782 North Orange Drive
Hollywood, CA 90028
Telephone: (213) 876-5080
credits: Family Plot—1976, Herbie Goes to Monte Carlo—1977, The North Avenue Irregulars—1979

STORARO, Vittorio, A.I.C.
credits: The Conformist—1970, Last Tango in Paris—1972, Apocalypse Now—1979, Reds—1981

SLOCOMBE, Douglas, B.S.C.
Contact: British Society of Cinematographers
158-160 Arthur Rd., Wimbleton Park
London SW 19, 8AQ England
credits: Raiders of the Lost Ark—1981, The Pirates of Penzance—1982

WEXLER, Haskel, A.S.C.
Business: Wexler/Hall Productions
716 North Alfred Street
Los Angeles, CA 90069
Telephone: (213) 655-6800
credits: America, America—1966, Who's Afraid of Virginia Woolf—1966, In the Heat of the Night—1967, The Graduate—1968, The Thomas Crown Affair—1968, Medium Cool—1969, Carnal Knowledge—1971, American Graffiti—1973, Bound for Glory *(academy award)*—1975, Coming Home—1979, Second Hand Hearts—1980

WILLIS, Gordon, A.S.C.
Agent: Phil Gersh Agency
222 North Canon Drive, Suite 201
Beverly Hills, CA 90210
Telephone: (213) 274-6611
credits: Klute—1971, The Godfather—1972, The Godfather, Part II—1974, The Parallax View—1974, The Paper Chase—19__, The Drowning Pool—19__, All The President's Men—1976, 9/30/55—1977, Annie Hall—1977, Comes a Horseman—1979, Interiors—1979, Stardust Memories—1980, Pennies From Heaven—1981

ZSIGMOND, Vilmos, A.S.C.
Agent: Smith/Gosnell Agency
20154 Pacific Coast Highway
Malibu, CA 90265
Telephone: (213) 456-6641
credits: McCabe and Mrs. Miller—1971, Images—1972, Deliverance—1973, Scarecrow—1973, The Long Goodbye—1973, Cinderella Liberty—1974, The Sugarland Express—1974, Obsession—1976, Close Encounters of the Third Kind *(academy award, best cinematography)*—1977, The Deer Hunter—1978, The Rose—1979, Winter Kills—1979, Heaven's Gate—1980, The Border—1982, Tough Enough—1982, Table For Five—1983

STUDIO EXECUTIVES

COLUMBIA PICTURES
Columbia Plaza
Burbank, CA 91505
Tel. (213) 954-6000

711 Fifth Avenue
New York, NY 10022
Tel: (212) 751-4400

Francis T. Vincent, Jr.
President, Columbia Pictures Industries

Frank Price
Chairman and President

Victor Kaufman
Vice Chairman

Marvin Antonowsky
President, Marketing and Research

Jonathan Dolgen
*President, Pay-Cable and Home
Entertainment Group*

James Spitz
President, Domestic Distribution

John Veitch
President, Columbia Pictures Productions

Patrick Williamson
*President, Columbia Pictures
International*

Eli Horowitz
Executive Vice President

Arnold Messer
*Executive Vice President, Worldwide
Business Affairs*

Kenneth Blancato
Senior Vice President, Advertising

Peter C. Kells
*Senior Vice President, Finance and
Administration*

Edward Roginski
*Senior Vice President, Domestic Publicity
and Promotion*

Tom McCarthy
Senior Vice President, Post Production

Stephen Randall
Senior Vice President, Research

Sheldon Schrager
*Senior Vice President, Production and
Executive Production Manager*

Linda Berken
Vice President–Talent Relations

John Byers
*Vice President, Creative Affairs and
Executive Story Editor, West Coast*

Robert Lawrence
Vice President, Production

Wendie Margolis
Vice President and Assistant to Chairman

Jennifer Shull
Vice President, Talent

Mary Cross
Story Editor

Diane Harmon-Asher
Story Editor, East Coast

Anne Kramer
Story Editor

WALT DISNEY PRODUCTIONS
500 South Buena Vista St.
Burbank, CA 91521
Tel. (213) 840-1000

Cardon Walker
*Chairman of the Board,
Chief Executive Officer*

Ron Miller
President and Chief Operating Officer

Thomas L. Wilhite
*Vice President, Motion Picture and
Television Production*

Robert Gibeaut
Vice President, Studio Operations

James B. Garber
*Vice President, Marketing, Motion Picture
and Television*

Robert King
Vice President, Marketing Planning

David Ehrman
Director of Creative Development

Gary Graf
Story Editor

Jack Lindquest
*Senior Vice President in charge of Advertising
and Publicity*

Erwin Okun
Vice President, Public Relations

Ron Cayo
Senior Vice President, Business Affairs

Michael Bagnall
Senior Vice President, Finance

Ted Schilz
Executive Production Manager

William Yates
Vice President, Television Production

METRO-GOLDWYN-MAYER FILM COMPANY
10202 W. Washington Blvd.
Culver City, CA 90230
Tel. (213) 558-5000

Frank Rothman
Chairman and Chief Executive Officer,
MGM/UA Entertainment

Frank Rosenfelt
Chairman of the Board and Chief
Executive Officer, MGM Film Co.

Donald Sipes
President and Chief Operating Officer

Karla Davidson
Vice President and General
Counsel-Entertainment

Frank I. Davis
Vice President, Business Affairs

Roger Mayer
Vice President, Administration

Walter C. Hoffer
Vice President and Treasurer

MGM MOTION PICTURE PRODUCTION DIVISION

Freddie Fields
President, Motion Picture Division

David Chasman
Executive Vice President in charge of
Worldwide Theatrical Production

John B. Tarnoff
Senior Vice President, Motion Picture
Production and Development

Lynn Arost
Vice President, Production

Gary Bell
Vice President, Post Production

Boaty Boatwright
Vice President, East Coast Production

Joseph D'Agosta
Vice President, Talent

George Justin
Vice President-Production Manager

Rosalie Muskatt
Vice President, East Coast
Creative Affairs

Madeline Warren
Vice President, Production

Sanford Climan
Production Executive

Lynn Goldman
East Coast Story Editor

Candace Lawrence
West Coast Story Editor

Joseph A. Fischer
President, MGM/UA Entertainment Co.

James D. Aljian
Senior Vice President-Financial Planning,
MGM/UA Entertainment Co.

Dean Stolber
Vice President, MGM/UA
Entertainment Co.

Jerry Esbin
President, MGM/UA Distribution
and Marketing Division

Jack Gordon
Senior Vice President, MGM/UA
International Distribution Division

studio executives

PARAMOUNT PICTURES CORPORATION

WEST COAST STUDIO:
5555 Melrose Avenue
Los Angeles, CA 90038
Tel. (213) 468-5000

NEW YORK HEADQUARTERS:
1 Gulf & Western Plaza
New York, NY 10023
Tel. (212) 333-4600

Barry Diller
Chairman of the Board and Chief
Executive Officer

Michael D. Eisner
President and Chief Operating Officer,
Motion Picture Division

Robert Peters
Senior Vice President, Corporate Division

Richard Zimbert
Senior Vice President and Assistant to
the President

Donald C. Simpson
President, Production, Motion Picture
Division

Ralph Kamon
Senior Vice President, Business and
Legal Affairs

Jeffrey Katzenberg
Senior Vice President, Production,
Motion Picture Division

Laurence M. Mark
Vice President, Production

Pam Dixon
Vice President, Production

Richard Fischoff
Vice President, Production

Dawn Steel
Vice President, Production

Charles Maguire
Vice President and Executive Production
Manager

Frank Bodo
Vice President, Production Finance

Joseph Adelman
Vice President in charge of
Business Affairs

Susan Pile
Vice President, Publicity & Promotion,
West Coast

Marcy Bolotin
Director, West Coast Publicity
and Promotion

Gordon Weaver
Senior Vice President, Marketing

Frank Mancuso
President, Paramount Distribution

Marvin Kutner
Senior Vice President, Domestic
Distribution

Lora Lee
Supervisor, Story Department

Dan Sherkow
Vice President, Paramount Theatre
Productions

TWENTIETH CENTURY-FOX FEATURE FILM DIVISION

WEST COAST STUDIO:
10201 W. Pico Boulevard
Los Angeles, CA 90064
Tel. (213) 277-2211

NEW YORK OFFICE:
49 West 57th Street
New York, NY 10019
Tel. (212) 750-1200

Marvin Davis
Owner, 20th Century-Fox

Alan Hirschfield
Chairman and Chief Executive Officer

Norman Levy
*Vice Chairman and President of
20th Century-Fox Entertainment*

C. Joseph LaBonte
*President and Chief Operating Officer,
Member of the Board*

Sherry Lansing
*President of 20th Century-Fox
Productions*

Robert W. Cort
Senior Vice President of Productions

Henry Guettel
*Senior Vice President of Production,
New York Office*

Richard Berger
*Senior Vice President of Worldwide
Production*

David Field
*Executive Vice President of Worldwide
Production*

Claire Townsend
Vice President of Production

Herb Wallerstein
*Vice President of Production
Management*

Susan Merzbach
Vice President of Creative Affairs

Richard Ingber
Vice President, Advertising

Lorna Darmour
*Vice President of Creative Affairs,
New York*

Laurie Spitz
Executive Story Editor

Dave Madden
Story Editor

Sara Devonshire
Story Editor, New York

Leon Brachman
Executive Vice President, Production

Raymond McCafferty
*Executive Vice President and General
Sales Manager*

Irving Ivers
*Executive Vice President, Advertising,
Publicity and Promotion*

Barry Lorie
*Senior Vice President of Publicity and
Promotion*

Elisabeth Landon
Vice President of Publicity

UNITED ARTISTS CORPORATION
WEST COAST OFFICES:
**3910 Overland Avenue
Culver City, CA 90230
Tel. (213) 202-0202**

NEW YORK HEADQUARTERS:
**729 Seventh Avenue
New York City, NY 10019
Tel. (212) 575-3000**

Frank Rothman
*Chairman and Chief Operating Officer,
MGM/UA Entertainment Co.*

David Begelman
*Chairman of the Board, United Artists
Corporation; Vice Chairman, MGM/UA
Entertainment Co.*

Dean Stolber
Executive Vice President

Benjamin Acker
Vice President, Taxes

Richard R. Bruning
Vice President and Treasurer

Harold E. Samboy
Vice President and Controller

Mauro A. Sardi
Vice President, Finance

Herbert T. Schottenfeld
Vice President and General Counsel

UNITED ARTISTS MOTION PICTURE PRODUCTION DIVISION

Paula Weinstein
President

Jon Gumpert
Senior Vice President, Business Affairs

Dennis Brown
Vice President, Production Management

Lawrence Erbst
Vice President, Business Affairs

Willie Hunt
Vice President, Production

Derek Kavanagh
Vice President, Production Management

Lee Katz
Vice President, Production

Michael Nathanson
Vice President, Production

Anthea Sylbert
Vice President, Production

Michael Barlow
Director of Creative Affairs, West Coast

Terri Farnsworth
Story Editor, West Coast

William Contardi
Director of Literary Affairs, East Coast

United Artists is a subsidiary of MGM/UA Entertainment Co.

UNIVERSAL PICTURES
100 Universal City Plaza
Universal City, CA 91608
Tel. (213) 985-4321

Lew Wasserman
Chairman of the Board and Chief Executive Officer

Sidney J. Sheinberg
President and Chief Operating Officer of MCA, Inc.

Thomas Wertheimer
Vice President of MCA, Inc., Senior Corporate Executive

Ned Tanen
President, Universal Pictures

Thom Mount
Executive Vice President in charge of Production

Hilton Green
Vice President, Production

Fred Brost
Vice President, Production

Sean Daniel
Vice President, Production

Verna Fields
Vice President, Production

Marianne Moloney
Vice President, Production

Helena Hacker
Vice President, Production

Annette Wells
Vice President of Literary Affairs

Robert Rehme
President, Distribution and Marketing

Robert Sherwood
Vice President, Distribution and Marketing

David Weitzner
Executive Vice President, Distributing and Marketing

Bob Chmiel
Story Editor, West Coast

studio executives

WARNER BROS.
4000 Warner Boulevard
Burbank, CA 91522
Tel. (213) 954-6000

Robert A. Daly
Chairman of the Board,
  Chief Executive Officer

Terry Semel
President, Chief Operating Officer

Frank Wells
Vice Chairman

Robert Shapiro
President, Theatrical Production Division

Mark Canton
Vice President of Production

Mark Rosenberg
Vice President of Production

Lucy Fisher
Vice President of Production

Ralph Peterson
Vice President and Treasurer

Fred T. Gallo
Executive Vice President, Worldwide
  Production

Jack Freedman
Vice President for Product Acquisition and
  Worldwide Business Affairs

Marion Dougherty
Vice President in charge of Talent
  and Casting

Leslie Morgan
West Coast Story Editor

Sandy Reisenbach
Executive Vice President, Worldwide
  Advertising and Publicity

Barry Reardon
President and General Sales Manager,
  Domestic Distribution

PRODUCTION COMPANY EXECUTIVES

production co. executives, motion picture

ABC MOTION PICTURES
2040 Avenue of the Stars
Los Angeles, CA 90067
Tel.: (213) 557-7777
Brandon Stoddard—President
Robert Bookman—Vice President,
Worldwide Production
Herb Jellinek—Vice President of
Production, ABC Entertainment
and ABC Motion Pictures
Philip Blumberg—Vice President of
Creative Affairs
Candace Farrell—Vice President,
Advertising/Publicity/Promotion
Barbara Sachs—Development Executive
Patty Newburger—Creative Affairs
Executive, East Coast
Gene Margolius—Producers
Representative

AMERICAN CINEMA PRODUCTIONS
6601 Romaine Street
Los Angeles, CA 90028
Tel. (213) 465-2100
Norman B. Katz—Chairman of the
Board
Andrew D. T. Pfeffer—President and
Chief Operating Officer
Jerrold T. Brandt, Jr.—Executive Vice
President

**ARKOFF INTERNATIONAL
PRODUCTIONS**
9200 West Sunset Boulevard
Los Angeles, CA 90069
Tel. (213) 278-7600
Samuel Z. Arkoff—President

**ASSOCIATED FILM DISTRIBUTION
(AFD)**
100 Universal City Plaza
Universal City, CA 91608
Tel. (213) 508-2665
Leo Greenfield—Vice President,
Marketing

**BERCOVICI-
ST. JOHN'S PRODUCTIONS**
10202 West Washington Blvd.
Culver City, CA 90230
Tel.: (213) 558-5000
Eric Bercovici—Executive Producer
Richard St. Johns—Executive Producer

BROOKSFILMS, LTD.
Offices: Zoetrope Studios
1040 North Las Palmas
Los Angeles, CA 90038
Tel. (213) 203-1375
Mel Brooks—President
Randy Auerbach—Editor, Research and
Development

CANNON GROUP, INC.
6464 Sunset Blvd., Suite 1150
Los Angeles, CA 90028
Tel. (213) 469-8124
Menahem Golan—Chairman of
the Board
Yoram Globus—President
Thomas Berman—Executive Vice
President, Domestic Distribution
Dan Dimbort—Vice President of
Foreign Sales
Priscilla MacDonald—Vice President,
Advertising & Publicity
David Womack—Production Manager

CARSON FILMS
Office: 4121 Radford Avenue
Studio City, CA 91604
Tel: (213) 506-8211
John J. McMahon—President of Carson
Films and Carson Productions
Marcia Nasatir—Vice President
Susan Whipple—Director of
Development
Charles Kaufman—Story Editor

CBS THEATRICAL FILMS DIVISION
Studio Center
4024 Radford Avenue
Studio City, CA 91604
Tel. (213) 760-5000
William Self—President,
CBS Theatrical Films
Richard A. Roth—Vice President of
Production
Nancy Hardin—Vice President of
Production
Robert Benard—Vice President of
Creative Affairs
Gary McCarthy—Vice President,
Finance
Gabe Sumner—President, Distribution
Lindsley Parsons—Vice President,
Executive Production Manager
Kathrin Seitz—Vice President, East
Coast Development
David Saunders—Vice President,
Business Affairs
Ron Yerxa—Director of Development
Harry Chotiner—Story Editor
Ian Jessel—Vice President of
International Distribution
Jonathan Kramer—Vice President,
Ancillary Rights
Leonard Morpurgo—Director of
International Advertising
Martin Garcia—Vice President of
Administration

CINEMA GROUP, INC.
Production/Financing Co.)8758
Venice Blvd.
Los Angeles, CA 90034
Tel: (213) 204-0102
William J. Immerman—President and
Chairman of the Board
Richard James—Senior Vice President,
Finance
Venetia Stevens—Vice President in
Charge of Production

CROWN INTERNATIONAL PICTURES
292 South La Cienega Blvd.
Beverly Hills, CA 90211
Telephone: (213) 657-6700
Mark Tenser—President
Mitchell Blum—General Sales Manager
Albert Giles—Vice President, Business
Affairs
Terry Myerson—Controller
John C. Calhoun—Director of
Advertising & Publicity
Jon Douglas—Director of Pay Television

EMBASSY PICTURES
956 Seward Street
Los Angeles, CA 90038
Tel.: (213) 460-7200
New York Office:
Embassy Pictures
300 East 42nd Street
New York, NY 10017
Tel.: (212) 949-8900

Alan Horn—Chairman, Embassy
Communications
Charles Weber—President, Embassy
Communications
Jeff Young, —Senior Vice President of
Creative Affairs
Roger Burlage—Senior Vice President
of Finance
Peter Bierstadt—Senior Vice President
of Legal and Business Affairs
Michael Glick—Vice President in charge
of Production
Nathan Chianta—Vice President,
Administration
William Shields—Vice President of
Distribution, General Sales Manager
Edward Crane—National Publicity
Director
Ken Goodman—National Advertising
Director
Mel Richmon—National Promotion
Director

production co. executives, motion picture

EMBASSY PICTURES, *continued*

Walter Keenan—Director of
Post Production
Leslie Pound—Director of International
Advertising & Publicity
Rolf Mittweg—President of International
Distribution and Marketing
*EMBASSY PICTURES is a joint venture
of Norman Lear and Jerry Perenchio*

EMI FILMS, INC.
9489 Dayton Way
Beverly Hills, CA 90210
Telephone: (213) 278-4770
HEADQUARTERS:
142 Wardour Street
London, England

Barry Spikings—President
John Kohn—Vice President
Norma Jackson—Vice President
Desi Rapp—Story Editor

FILMCREST INTERNATIONAL CORP.
595 Madison Avenue
New York, NY 10019
Telephone: (212) ~~371-4620~~ 310-1500
SBIC - Sund pix at a Standstill now

Pedro Teitelbaum—President

FILMWAYS PICTURES
1875 Century Park East, Suite 300
Los Angeles, CA 90067
Tel. (213) 557-8700

Arthur Krim—Chairman
Eric Pleskow—President and Chief
Executive Officer
William Bernstein—Executive Vice
President
Mike Medavoy—Executive Vice
President
Julie Kirkham—Director of Creative
Affairs
Ernst Goldschmidt—Senior Vice
President of International Operations
Lloyd Leipzig—Senior Vice President,
Publicity and Exploitation
Robert Geary—Vice President

Fred Goldberg—Senior Vice President
(Filmways becomes Orion Pictures
Corporation in the Fall)

GOLDEN HARVEST FILMS
8 Hammerhill Road
Kowloon, Hong Kong
Telephone: 275-155

Raymond Chow—President
Andre Morgan—Head of Production
Charles O. Glenn—Vice President of
World Wide Advertising–Publicity–
Promotion

HEMDALE LEISURE CORP.
9255 Sunset Boulevard
Los Angeles, CA 90069
Telephone (213) 550-6894

John Daly—President
*Hemdale Leisure Corp. is part of the
London based Hemdale Leisure Group*

THE INDIE PROD COMPANY
10201 West Pico Boulevard, Bldg. 86
Los Angeles, CA 90035
Telephone: (213) 203-3241

Daniel Melnick—President
Allen Adler—Vice President
Craig Zadan—Creative Executive

INTER MEDIA ENTERTAINMENT CO.
10202 West Washington Blvd.
Culver City, CA 90230
Telephone: (213) 558-6100

Fred Silverman—President
George Reeves—Vice President
Lin Bolen—Vice President, Creative
Affairs

IPC FILMS
10201 West Pico Blvd.
Los Angeles, CA 90064
Tel. (213) 277-2211

Bruce Gilbert—President
Eileen Peterson—Vice President of
Creative Affairs
Jane Fonda—Executive Producer

JENSEN FARLEY PICTURES
556 East 200 South
Salt Lake City, Utah 84102
California Office:
12711 Ventura Blvd., Suite 410
Studio City, CA 91604
Raylan Jensen—President
Clair Farley—Vice President
Ron Rodgers—Vice President

THE LADD COMPANY
4000 Warner Blvd.
Burbank, CA 91522
Tel. (213) 954-4400
Alan Ladd, Jr.—President
Gareth Wigan—Vice President
Jay Kanter—Vice President
Leonard Kroll—Vice President,
   Production Operations
Joseph Graham—Vice President of
   Business Affairs
Allyn Stewart—Vice President of
   Creative Affairs
Sarah Altshul—Vice President of
   Creative Affairs
Ashley Boone—Vice President of
   Marketing & Distribution
Bob Dingilian—Vice President,
   Advertising, Publicity & Promotions
Burt Morrison—Vice President,
   Finance & Administration
John Goldwyn—Story Editor

LORIMAR
3970 Overland Avenue
Culver City, CA 90230
Tel. (213) 202-2000
New York Office:
Lorimar Productions
15 Columbus Circle, 8th Floor
New York, NY 10023
(212) 541-9200
Merv Adelson—Chairman of the Board
Lee Rich—President

Carol Baum—Vice President of Feature
   Film Development
Bridget Potter—Vice President/Film & TV
   Development (New York)
Rosanne Ehrlich—East Coast Story
   Editor
Bernard Weitzman—Executive Vice
   President/Administration
J. Anthony Young—Chief Financial
   Officer, Senior Vice President
Edward O. Denault—Vice President,
   Production (Film/TV)
Miguel Tejada Flores—Vice President,
   Film Development
Malcolm Stuart—Vice President, Movies
   of the Week/Mini-series Film
Barbara Miller—Vice President, Casting
Susan Dalsimer—Executive Story Editor
   (New York)
Melvin Jacobs—Lorimar Research
Larry Sugar—President of Lorimar
   Distribution International
*(For Lorimar Television—see Production
Co.'s, Movies for Television)*

LUCASFILM, LTD.
P.O. Box 2009
San Rafael, CA 94902
Tel. (415) 457-5282
George Lucas—Chairman of the Board
Robert Greber—President and Chief
   Executive Officer
Roger Faxon—Vice President and Chief
   Operating Officer
Howard Kazanjian—Vice President
   of Production
Chris Kalabokes—Vice President
   of Finance
Sidney Ganis—Executive Vice President,
   Marketing and Publicity
Bobbe Tyler—Director of Administration

MARBLE ARCH PRODUCTIONS
12711 Ventura Blvd.
Studio City, CA 91604
Tel. (213) 760-2110

MARBLE ARCH, *continued*

Robert Holmes A'Cort—Chairman of the
  Board of ACC
Howard Alston—Vice President and
  Executive Production Manager
Earl Wroten—Production Executive
Stuart Mandel—Vice President, Business
  Affairs
Ralph Rivera—Vice President, Chief
  Financial Officer
Regina Gruss—Vice President,
  Advertising and Publicity
Glenda Grant—Vice President,
  Personnel and Administration

THE MIRISCH CORPORATION
3966 Overland Avenue
Culver City, CA 90230
Tel.: (213) 559-2593

Marvin Mirisch—Chairman of the Board
Walter Mirisch—President
*The Mirisch Corp. has a producer
contract agreement to make films for
United Artists*

MMA
8484 Wilshire Blvd.
Beverly Hills, CA 902__
Tel.: (213) 852-1956

Steven Bach—President
Mimi Roth—Vice President,
  Development
Laurence Minkoff—Story Editor

MOTOWN PRODUCTIONS
6255 Sunset Boulevard, 18th Floor
Los Angeles, CA 90028
Tel: (213) 468-3500

Berry Gordy—Chairman, Motown
  Industries
Suzanne De Passe—President
Carol Caruso—Vice President,
  Acquisitions
Suzanne Coston—Vice President,
  Music Division

MTM ENTERPRISES PRODUCTIONS
4024 Radford Avenue
Studio City, CA 91604
Tel: (213) 760-5000

Arthur Price—President
Stuart Irwin—Vice President in charge
of Creative Affairs

NEUFELD-DAVIS PRODUCTIONS
9454 Wilshire Blvd.
Beverly Hills, CA 90212
Tel.: (213) 858-2929

Mace Neufeld—President
Thomas H. Brodek—Executive Vice
  President
Derek Peter—Vice President of
  International Sales
Peter Exline—Director of Creative
  Affairs
Bobbi Fletcher—Business Affairs
  and Legal
Lucy Schneider—Co-ordinator of
  Business Affairs

NEW WORLD PICTURES
11600 San Vicente
Los Angeles, CA 90049
Tel. (213) 820-6733

Roger Corman—President
Paul Almond—Executive Vice
  President and Chief
  Operating Officer
Roger Lewin—General Sales Manager
Jane Covner—Director of Publicity
  and Promotion

POLYGRAM PICTURES
3940 Overland Avenue
Culver City, CA 90230
Tel. (213) 202-4400

Gordon Stulberg—President
Jere Henshaw—Executive Vice
  President, Worldwide Production
Alan Wilson—Vice President, Production
  Administration

POLYGRAM PICTURES, *continued*
Nancy Goliger—Vice President,
  Worldwide Advertising & Publicity
Mike Biscio—Vice President, Worldwide
  Marketing
Jim Johnson—Executive Vice President,
  Chief Financial Officer
Adam Fields—Vice President of
  Production
Daniel Marquet—Vice President, Foreign
  Marketing
Don Mirisch—Vice President, Business
  Affairs

RASTAR FILMS, INC.
300 Colgems Square
Burbank, CA 91505
Tel. (213) 954-6000

Ray Stark—Chairman of the Board
Guy McElwaine—President of Rastar
  Films
Phil Feldman—Executive Vice President
Larry Marks—Senior Vice President of
  Production
John Fiedler—Vice President of
  Production and Development
William Sackheim—Vice President of
  Production
Richard Lyon—President of Rastar TV
*Rastar is a subsidiary of Columbia
Pictures*

RKO PICTURES
1440 Broadway
New York, NY 10018
Tel. (212) 764-7000

C. Robert Manby—President
Shane O'Neil—Vice President

RSO FILMS:
CALIFORNIA OFFICE:
5555 Melrose Avenue
Los Angeles, CA 90038
Tel. (213) 468-5000

NEW YORK OFFICE:
1775 Broadway
New York, New York 10019
Tel. (212) 975-0766

Robert Stigwood—President

SHERWOOD PRODUCTIONS
MGM Studios
10202 West Washington Blvd.
Culver City, CA 90230
Telephone: (213) 836-3000

Herbert F. Solow—
Alan E. Salke—
Bruce McNall—
Peter Duchow—Senior Vice President

**SIMON/REEVES/LANDSBURG
PRODUCTIONS, INC.**
260 South Beverly Drive
Beverly Hills, CA 90212
Tel. (213) 273-5450

Melvin Simon—Chairman of the
  Executive Committee
Milton Goldstein—Chairman and Chief
  Executive Officer
Howard Lipstone—Vice Chairman
Alan Landsburg—President
Keith G. Fleer—Executive Vice President
Frank McKevitt—Executive Vice
  President
John F. Rubinich—Vice President,
  Worldwide Sales Manager
Cheryl E. Boone—Vice President in
  charge of Worldwide Advertising
  and Publicity
Dayle Michelle—Vice President in
  charge of Creative Affairs
Juan Molina—Treasurer and Chief
  Financial Officer
Alan Myerson—Secretary and General
  Counsel

ZANUCK/BROWN COMPANY
BEVERLY HILLS OFFICE:
P.O. Box 900
Beverly Hills, CA 90213
Tel. (213) 277-2211

ZANUCK/BROWN CO., *continued*
NEW YORK OFFICE:
40 W. 57th Street
New York, NY 10019
Tel. (212) 977-5500

Richard Zanuck—President
David Brown—Vice President
Joy Kaplan—Story Editor

ZOETROPE STUDIOS
SAN FRANCISCO OFFICE:
916 Kearny Street
San Francisco, CA 94133
Tel. (415) 788-7500
LOS ANGELES STUDIO:
1040 North Las Palmas
Los Angeles, CA 90038
Tel. (213) 463-7191

Robert Spiotta—President
Ben Bereslaur—Chief Financial Officer
Fred Roos—Vice President,
    Development
Ben Cowitt—Vice President and General
    Manager, Hollywood General Studios
Alex Carter—Director of Personnel
Tom Luddy—Head of Special Projects
Francis Coppola—Artistic Director

*Zoetrope Studios is owned by Francis
Coppola*

PART II

MOVIES MADE FOR TELEVISION SECTION

THE 10 BEST TV-MOVIES
By Judith Crist

Another TV-movie year has gone through, if not down, the tube and it's once again time for stock-taking and 10 Best listing.

1981 was the 15th year of tailored-for-television movies and the first in which as much as $5 million was spent on the making of a one-shot (i.e., non-miniseries) film—the excellent "Kent State." Movies for the small as well as the large screen are, of course, more expensive by the year; they're also longer—and fewer. There were 122 new TV films shown in 1981 (137 were shown the previous year), with NBC providing 44 (eight more than in 1980), CBS showing 54 (eight fewer than the year before), ABC offering 23 (down by 13) and PBS one (down from three).

Why the decline? The Writers Guild of America strike, lasting from April 11 through July 14, had little effect on TV-movies; in anticipation of the strike, in fact, the networks had stockpiled movie scripts. What was affected were the new fall series, and early-season TV-movies filled in for those that were not ready. At the same time, however, the networks have cut back to only five prime-time movie slots a week; and on weekends, one spokesman noted, the tendency is to use theatrical films. The "unofficial" explanation for this is "the better to fight cable competition."

If there were trends to be spotted, the most obvious was further emphasis on the fact-based drama, both personal and social. The adapting of novels and the rehashing of old plays and movies, rarely with improvement on the originals, continued. Drama and melodrama prevailed: once again there was a dearth of comedy—intended comedy, that is.

The stars came out for biography. Faye Dunaway was on hand in "Evita Peron"; Ellen Burstyn was a knockout as the accused killer of the Scarsdale Diet Doctor in "The People vs. Jean Harris"; Jamie Lee Curtis was the Playboy playmate in "Death of a Centerfold: The Dorothy Stratten Story"; Annette O'Toole was Tammy Wynette in "Stand By Your Man"; Jaclyn Smith went from schoolgirl to widow as "Jacqueline Bouvier Kennedy"; Glenda Jackson starred in "The Patricia Neal Story," Cicely Tyson in "The Marva Collins Story"; and Robert Foxworth and Anthony Hopkins portrayed the Apostles in "Peter and Paul." Mickey Rooney triumphed twice, as a cancer-ridden circus clown in "Leave 'Em Laughing" and as a retarded man in "Bill,"

both fact-based stories. Bette Davis gave backbone and style to "Family Reunion," a pleasant fiction.

The films dealing with actual events were far more lavish—and effective—than the docudramas of yesteryear, although there are still those critical of the blend of fact with fiction for purposes of drama. Beyond the five on my 10 Best list, there were re-creations of the last days of Hitler in "The Bunker"; the rescue of six Americans in "Escape from Iran: The Canadian Caper"; the escape of East Germans in "Berlin Tunnel 21"; and the American Olympic hockey triumph in "Miracle on Ice."

There were remakes of "Madame X," "Splendor in the Grass," "Midnight Lace," "Dial 'M' for Murder," "Of Mice and Men" and even of "Jacqueline Susann's Valley of the Dolls '1981'." Anent the last, there were other trash wallows, cued apparently by the popularity of soaps and *Dallas*, all about the rotten rich, ranging from the delicious, fact-based "Murder in Texas" and "The Million-Dollar Face" down to the imperfectly awful "Mistress of Paradise" and "Golden Gate."

Physical suffering and social issues were not slighted. Various aspects of rape were exploited in several films; abortion was dealt with thoughtfully in "The Choice"; abandoned children were the concern of "Broken Promise," "The Children Nobody Wanted" and "A Long Way Home." Johnny Cash did his bit for illiteracy in "The Pride of Jesse Hallam"; gun control was considered in "A Gun in the House," anorexia nervosa in "The Best Little Girl in the World," polygamy in "Child Bride of Short Creek," chemical poisons in "Bitter Harvest," drugs in "Angel Dusted," teen-age pregnancy in "Born to Be Sold," and "special" children in "The Acorn People."

Television stars and series were exploited in a number of films whose titles told all: "The Brady Girls Get Married"; "The Munsters' Revenge"; "The Harlem Globetrotters on Gilligan's Island"; "Return of the Beverly Hillbillies." There were pilots and would-be pilots. And out of the 122 movies of the year, there were about 40 that were watchable. How many were memorable?

To each his own. Herewith, my personal list of the 10 top TV-movies of 1981. Rather than compare the incomparable, I offer them in chronological order:

Crisis at Central High, written by Richard Levinson and William Link and directed by Lamont Johnson, turns the Supreme Court–ordered 1957 integration of that Little Rock, Ark., school into an absorbing, suspense-laden drama, its focal point Joanne Woodward's Elizabeth Huckaby, a school administrator embodying the heroism of ordinary people whose extraordinary spirit and strength of character sustain us in times of crisis. (CBS)

Kent State, written by Gerald Green and Richard Kramer and directed by James Goldstone, dramatizes the events on that Ohio campus that culminated in the killing of four students by National Guardsmen on May 4, 1970; and does so in such fairminded, balanced detail that final judgments are ours in this stunning reminder of the climactic tragedy of the '60s, that "decade that began in innocence and ended in despair." (NBC)

Fallen Angel, written by Lew Hunter and directed by Robert Lewis, deals with the potentially sensational subject of child pornography with intelligence, taste and social conscience. Its emphasis is on the vulnerability of the neglected child, its warning directed to the well-intentioned but preoccupied parent. Melinda Dillon and Dana Hill as mother and child and Richard Masur as the pedophile bring a noteworthy honesty to a sensitive subject. (CBS)

The Private History of a Campaign That Failed was adapted by Philip Reisman Jr. from Mark Twain's autobiographical Civil War short story about 15 youngsters from Hannibal, Mo., who organize their own militia to drive out the Yankees. Directed by Peter H. Hunt, this charming and powerful period piece captures Twain's humor and ironic perception of youngsters stirred by patriotic fervor who get their first and bitter taste of combat.

The Sophisticated Gents, adapted by Melvin Van Peebles from a John A. Williams novel and directed by Harry Falk, uses the reunion of ghetto sandlot athletes celebrating their coach's retirement not only to consider the yield of the urban ghetto's "roots" but also to offer perceptive truths about middle-class life. It does so in terms of a suspenseful drama, made riveting by an extraordinarily gifted cast. (NBC)

Mickey Spillane's Margin for Murder, with teleplay by Calvin Clements Jr. and direction by Daniel Haller, revives and revitalizes the tough-private-eye genre. With a story by Alex Lucas based on Spillane's characters, Kevin Dobson's Mike Hammer takes us into that moodsy, bluesy one-man-judge-and-jury world of the compassionate avenger ("Your friend gets killed, you do something about it") and we're safe home. (CBS)

Skokie, written by Ernest Kinoy and directed by Herbert Wise, goes beyond the re-creation of a controversial event—the attempt by neo-Nazis to demonstrate in a largely Jewish suburb of Chicago in 1977— to deal with the legal and moral issues at the heart of it. This effective and affecting drama of ideas forces a reassessment of our own faith in freedom for thought—particularly for that Holmesian "thought we hate." (CBS)

Of Mice and Men, adapted from the Steinbeck novel by E. Nick Alexander and directed by Reza Badiyi, transcends earlier screen and stage versions of this classic story of two Depression-era itinerant ranch hands. Its careful detailing of their life and the subtle enhancement of the secondary characters, with remarkable performances by Lew Ayres, Cassie Yates and others, add complexity to the compassion of the tragic climax. (NBC)

The Patricia Neal Story, written by Robert Anderson and directed by Anthony Harvey and Anthony Page, is a brilliantly dramatized true story, with Glenda Jackson as the actress who suffered a near-fatal stroke and Dirk Bogarde as her husband, Ronald Dahl, who literally forced her to recover. Their is an incredible story—and an exhilharating one—of dedication, love and the triumph of the will over physical disability. (CBS)

Bill, based by Corey Blechman on a true story by Barry Morrow and directed by Anthony Page, is the story of Bill Sackter, a mentally retarded middle-aged man, and Morrow, a young filmmaker who helps him achieve an independent life. Mickey Rooney is perfection as the "simple" man and Dennis Quaid irresistible as a man willing to be his brother's keeper. It's an inspiring story of friendship and responsibility, unsentimental but rich in honest sentiment. (CBS)

And my next 10 would be among "A Long Way Home," "Don't Look Back," "The Bunker," "Bitter Harvest," "Grambling's White Tiger," "The Choice," "Escape from Iran: The Canadian Caper," "Leave 'Em Laughing," "The Marva Collins Story," "Crazy Times," "The Killing of Randy Webster," "When the Circus Came to Town," maybe even "The Million-Dollar Face" and "Murder in Texas." The choices, as always, are yours.

—Reprinted with permission from TV Guide® Magazine. Copyright © 1982 by Triangle Publications, Inc.

DIRECTORS
MOVIES FOR TELEVISION

AARON, Paul
(see also Motion Picture Directors)
Agent: Lee Muhl, ICM
8899 Beverly Boulevard
Los Angeles, CA 90048
Telephone: (213) 550-4000

credits: The Miracle Worker (NBC)—1980, Thin Ice (CBS)—1981, Maid in America (CBS)—1982

ANTONIO, Lou
Agent: Creative Artists Agency
1888 Century Park East, Suite 1400
Los Angeles, CA 90067
Telephone: (213) 277-4545

credits: We're Fighting Back (CBS)—1981, The Star Maker (NBC)—1981

AVERBACK, Hy
Agent: Creative Artists Agency
1888 Century Park East, Suite 1400
Los Angeles, CA 90067
Telephone: (213) 277-4545

credits: Guide for the Married Woman—1978, The Girl, the Gold Watch and Dynamite (OPT)—1981

BADIYI, Reza
Agent: Agency for the Performing Arts
9000 Sunset Blvd., Suite 315
Los Angeles, CA 90069
Telephone: (213) 273-0744

credits: Of Mice and Men (ABC)—1981

BARTMAN, Bill
Agent: Scott Harris
The Phil Gersh Agency
222 North Canon Drive, Suite 201
Beverly Hills, CA 90210
Telephone: (213) 274-6611

credits: O'Hara's Wife—1981

BEAUMONT, Gabrielle
Agent: William Morris Agency
151 El Camino Drive
Beverly Hills, CA 90212
Telephone: (213) 274-7451

credits: Death of a Centerfold: The Dorothy Stratten Story (NBC)—1981

BLACK, Noel
Business: Highway Productions
120 Greenfield Avenue
Los Angeles, CA 90049
Telephone: (213) 476-4719
Agent: Chasin-Park-Citron

credits: The Other Victim (CBS)—1981, The Electric Grandmother (NBC), Cry of Innocence (CBS)

BRIDGES, Beau
Business: Cates/Bridges Co.
9200 Sunset Boulevard, Suite 913
Los Angeles, CA 90069
Telephone: (213) 273-7773

credits: The Kid from Nowhere (NBC)—1981

BROWN, Georg Stanford
Agent: ICM
8899 Beverly Boulevard
Los Angeles, CA 90048
Telephone: (213) 550-4000

credits: Roots–II—1978, Grambling's White Tiger—1981

BURROWS, James
(see also Motion Picture Directors)
Agent: Broder-Kurland Agency
9046 Sunset Boulevard
Los Angeles, CA 90069
Telephone: (213) 274-8921

credits: More Than Friends

directors, movies for television

CATES, Gilbert
(see also Motion Picture Directors)
Business: The Cates Brothers Co.
9200 Sunset Boulevard, Suite 913
Los Angeles, CA 90069
Telephone: (213) 273-7773

credits: Johnny We Hardly Knew Ye, After the Fall, The Affair, To All My Friends on Shore, Stubby Pringle's Christmas

CHAFFEY, Don
(see also Motion Picture Directors)
Business: Nicolette Productions
Telephone: (213) 851-0391

Agent: Contemporary-Korman Artists
132 Lasky Drive
Beverly Hills, CA 90212
Telephone: (213) 278-8250

credits: Gift of Love—1978, Code R—1981

CHOMSKY, Marvin
Agent: Creative Artists Agency
1888 Century Park East, Suite 1400
Los Angeles, CA 90067
Telephone: (213) 277-4545

credits: Holocaust—1978, Attica—1980, The Lilac Season—1981, Evita Peron—1981

COLLA, Richard
Agent: William Morris Agency
151 El Camino Drive
Beverly Hills, CA 90212
Telephone: (213) 274-7451

credits: Don't Look Back (ABC)—1981

COLLINS, Robert
Agent: Creative Artists Agency
1888 Century Park East, Suite 1400
Los Angeles, CA 90067
Telephone: (213) 277-4545

credits: Gideon's Trumpet—1980, Savage Harvest—1981, Our Family Business (ABC)—1981

CONRAD, William
Agent: Creative Artists Agency
1888 Century Park East, Suite 1400
Los Angeles, CA 90067
Telephone: (213) 277-4545

credits: Side Show (NBC)—1981

COOK, Fielder
Agent: Phil Gersh Agency
222 North Canon Drive, Suite 201
Beverly Hills, CA 90210
Telephone: (213) 274-6611

credits: Too Far to Go (NBC)—1979, Family Reunion (NBC)—1981

COOPER, Jackie
Business: Jackie Enterprises, Inc.
9621 Royalton Drive
Beverly Hills, CA 90210
Agent: Creative Artists Agency
1888 Century Park East, Suite 1400
Los Angeles, CA 90067
Telephone: (213) 277-4545

credits: Leave 'Em Laughing—1981, The Rosemary Clooney Story (CBS)—1982

CURTIS, Dan
(see also Producers, Movies for TV)
Business: Dan Curtis Productions
Paramount Studios
5555 Melrose Avenue
Los Angeles, CA 90038
Telephone: (213) 468-5000

credits: Mrs. R's Daughter (NBC)—1979, The Last Ride of the Dalton Gang (NBC)—1979, The Long Days of Summer (ABC)—1980, I Think I'm Having a Baby—1980, The Winds of War (ABC)—1982

DAMSKI, Melvin
  Agent: Phil Gersh Agency
  222 North Canon Drive, Suite 201
  Beverly Hills, CA 90210
  Telephone: (213) 274-6611

credits: Legend of Walks Far Woman, Long Journey Back, The Child Stealer—1981, American Dream—1981, For Ladies Only (NBC)—1981

DAY, Robert
  Agent: Creative Artists Agency
  1888 Century Park East, Suite 1400
  Los Angeles, CA 90067
  Telephone: (213) 277-4545

credits: Ritual of Evil, House on Greenapple Road, In Broad Daylight, Mr. and Mrs. Bo Jo Jones, Having Babies, Home of Our Own, Black Market Baby, Death Stalk, The Grass Is Always Greener, Peter and Paul—1981, Scruples (ABC)—1981

DeFELITTA, Frank
  Agent: Michael Marcus
  Creative Artists Agency
  1888 Century Park East, Suite 1400
  Los Angeles, CA 90067
  Telephone: (213) 277-4545

credits: The Night of the Scarecrow (CBS)—1981

DONNER, Clive
(see also Motion Picture Directors)
  Agent: William Morris Agency
  151 El Camino Drive
  Beverly Hills, CA 90212
  Telephone: (213) 274-7451

credits: Oliver Twist (CBS)—1982

DUBIN, Charles S.
  Agent: Creative Artists Agency
  1888 Century Park East, Suite 1400
  Los Angeles, CA 90067
  Telephone: (213) 277-4545

credits: Roots II—1978, Topper—1980, The Gathering, Part II—1981

DUKE, Daryl
  Agent: Jack Gilardi, ICM
  8899 Beverly Boulevard
  Los Angeles, CA 90048
  Telephone: (213) 550-4000

credits: I Heard the Owl Call My Name—1974, The Thorn Birds (miniseries)—1982

ELIKANN, Larry
  Business: The Larry Elikann Co.
  100 S. Doheny Drive
  Los Angeles, CA 90048
  Telephone: (213) 271-4406
  Agent: William Morris Agency
  151 El Camino Drive
  Beverly Hills, CA 90212
  Telephone: (213) 859-4471

credits: The Great Wallendas, Charlies Balloon, Palmerstown, USA (NBC)—1981, Falcon Crest—1982, Flamingo Road (2 hr.)—1982

ERMAN, John
  Agent: Creative Artists Agency
  1888 Century Park East, Suite 1400
  Los Angeles, CA 90067
  Telephone: (213) 277-4545
  Bus. Mgr.: Plant Cohen & Co.
  9777 Wilshire Blvd.
  Beverly Hills, CA 90212
  Telephone: 278-6171

credits: Letters from Three Lovers—1973, Green Eyes—1975, Roots—1977,

ERMAN, John, *continued*

Alexander, The Other Side of Dawn—1977, Roots, The Next Generations—1978, Child of Glass—1978, Just You and Me—1978, My Old Man—1980, The Secret Love of Marilyn Monroe (NBC)—1981, The Letter (ABC)—1981

FALK, Harry G. Jr.
Agent: William Morris Agency
151 El Camino Drive
Beverly Hills, CA 90212
Telephone: (213) 274-7451

credits: The Sophisticated Gents (NBC)—1981

FENADY, Georg J.
Agent: Jim Jacobson
Telephone: (213) 275-0804

credits: Hanging By a Thread—1978, Cave In—1979, The Night the Bridge Fell Down—1979

FORBES, Bryan
(see also Motion Picture Directors)
Agent: William Morris Agency
151 El Camino Drive
Beverly Hills, CA 90212
Telephone: (213) 274-7451

credits: The Slipper and the Rose, The Stepford Wives—1977, Goodbye Norma Jean—1979

FREEDMAN, Jerrold
(see also Motion Picture Directors)
Business: Chesapeake Films, Inc.
9220 Sunset Boulevard, Suite 206
Los Angeles, CA 90069
Telephone: (213) 275-3138

credits: Some Kind of Miracle—1979, This Man Stands Alone—1979, The Streets of L.A.—1979, The Boy Who Drank Too Much—1980, In Our Hands—1981, The Victims (ABC)—1982

GALFAS, Timothy
Agent: Shapiro-Lichtman
2049 Century Park East
Los Angeles, CA 90067
Telephone: (213) 557-2244

credits: A Case of Rape—1977, Man-eaters—1978

GETHERS, Steven
Agent: Adams, Ray & Rosenberg
9200 Sunset Boulevard, Penthouse 25
Los Angeles, CA 90069
Telephone: (213) 278-3000

credits: Billy, Portrait of a Street Kid (NBC), Father Damien, Leper Priest (NBC), Jacqueline Bouvier Kennedy (ABC)—1981

GOLDSTONE, James
Agent: Creative Artists Agency
1888 Century Park East, Suite 1400
Los Angeles, CA 90067
Telephone: (213) 277-4545

credits: A Clear and Present Danger—1969, Journey From Darkness, Eric, Things in Their Seasons, Studs Lonigan—1978, Kent State—1980, Bad Men—1982

GRAHAM, William
Agent: Creative Artists Agency
1888 Century Park East, Suite 1400
Los Angeles, CA 90067
Telephone: (213) 277-4545

credits: Birds of Prey II (CBS)—1982

GRAUMAN, Walter
Agent: Broder-Kurland Agency
9046 Sunset Boulevard
Los Angeles, CA 90069
Telephone: (213) 274-8921

credits: Jacqueline Susann's Valley of the Dolls—1981

GREEN, Guy
Agent: Phil Gersh Agency
222 North Canon Drive, Suite 201
Beverly Hills, CA 90210
Telephone: (213) 274-6611

credits: Dr. Meg Laurel (CBS), Jennifer (NBC), Jimmy B and Andre (CBS), Inmates: A Love Story (ABC)—1981, Isabel's Choice

GREENE, David
Business: David Greene Productions
4225 Coldwater Canyon
Studio City, CA 91604
Telephone: (213) 766-3547

credits: The People Next Door—1975, Count of Monte Cristo—1976, Rich Man, Poor Man—1976, Roots—1977, Trial of Lee Harvey Oswald—1980, Friendly Fire—1980, The Choice (CBS)—1981, World War III (CBS)—1981, Cold Reading (CBS)—1982

HALE, Billy
Agent: William Morris Agency
Personal Manager: Marvin Mickelson
Telephone: (213) 858-1097

credits: Red Alert, The Great Niagra, Stalk The Wild Child, Nightmare, How I Spent My Summer Vacation, Murder in Texas—1981

HALLER, Daniel
Agent: Irv Schechter
404 North Rosbury Drive
Beverly Hills, CA 90210
Telephone: (213) 278-8070

credits: Micky Spillane's Mike Hammer—1981

HARDY, Joseph
(see also Motion Picture Directors)
Agent: Bill Haber
Creative Artists Agency
1888 Century Park East, Suite 1400
Los Angeles, CA 90067
Telephone: (213) 277-4545

credits: The Day the Bubble Burst, Bliss, Loves Savage Fury, Not in Front of the Children, Love Is a Many Splendored Thing, Funny Papers, Man of Destiny, The Lady's Not For Burning, Great Expectations

HARRIS, Harry
Agent: Contemporary-Korman Artists
132 Lasky Drive
Beverly Hills, CA 90212
Telephone: (213) 278-8250

Business: Three H Productions
10999 Riverside Drive
North Hollywood, CA 91602
Telephone: (213) 769-7822

credits: The Runaways (CBS), Rivkin: Bounty Hunter (CBS)—1981

HARVEY, Anthony
(see also Motion Picture Directors)
Agent: William Morris Agency
151 El Camino Drive
Beverly Hills, CA 90212
Telephone: (213) 274-7451

credits: The Glass Menagerie, Gypsy House: The Patricia Neal Story (CBS)—1981, Svengali (CBS)—1982

HAYERS, Sidney
Agent: Shapiro-Lichtman
2049 Century Park E., Suite 1320
Los Angeles, CA 90067
Telephone: (213) 557-2244

credits: Seekers—1979, The Last Convertible—1979, Battlestar Galactica—1980, Condominium—1981

directors, movies for television

HEFFRON, Richard
(see also Motion Picture Directors)
  Agent: Creative Artists Agency
  1888 Century Park East, Suite 1400
  Los Angeles, CA 90067
  Telephone: (213) 277-4545

credits: The California Kid, The Morning After, I Will Fight No More Forever, See How She Runs, Young Joe Kennedy, A Rumor of War—1981, A Whale for the Killing—1981

HICKOX, Douglas
  Agent: Shapiro-Lichtman, Inc.
  2049 Century Park East, Suite 1320
  Los Angeles, CA 90067
  Telephone: (213) 557-2244

credits: The Phoenix—1981

HOLCOMB, Roderick
  Agent: Eisenbach, Greene, Duchow
  760 North La Cienega Boulevard
  Los Angeles, CA 90069
  Telephone: (213) 659-3420

credits: Just a Little Inconvenience, The Witching (ABC)—1981

HOOPER, Tobe
(see also Directors, Motion Pictures)
  Agent: Agency for the Performing Arts
  Telephone: (213) 273-0744

credits: Salem's Lot

HUNT, Peter H.
  Business: Peter Hunt Films, Inc.
  2229 Roscomare Road
  Los Angeles, CA 90024

credits: The Beasts in the Streets (NBC), The Private History of a Campaign That Failed (PBS)—1981

HOWARD, Ron
(see also Screenwriters)

Business: Major H Productions
5555 Melrose Avenue
Los Angeles, CA 90038
Telephone: (213) 465-5800

credits: Cotton Candy—1978, Tut and Tuttle—1979, Skyward—1980

HUSSEIN, Waris
  Agent: The Lantz Office
  114 East 55th Street
  New York, NY 10022
  Telephone: (212) 751-2107

credits: Edward and Mrs. Simpson—1980, And Baby Makes Six (NBC), The Henderson Monster (CBS), Callie and Son—1981

JAMESON, Jerry
  Agent: William Morris Agency
  151 El Camino Drive
  Beverly Hills, CA 90212
  Telephone: (213) 274-7451

credits: Stand By Your Man—1981, Hell and High Water (CBS)—1981, Killing at Hell's Gate (CBS)—1981

JOHNSON, Kenneth C.
  Atty.: Silverberg, Rosen, Leon & Behr
  Century Park East
  Los Angeles, CA 90067
  Telephone: (213) 277-4500

  Office: The Burbank Studios
  4000 Warner Boulevard
  Burbank, CA 91522
  Telephone: (213) 954-6000

credits: Senior Trip—1981

JOHNSON, Lamont
(see also Motion Picture Directors)
  Agent: John Gaines, A.P.A.
  9000 Sunset Blvd., Suite 315
  Los Angeles, CA 90069
  Telephone: (213) 273-0744

JOHNSON, Lamont, *continued*

credits: My Sweet Charlie—1970, That Certain Summer—1973, The Execution of Private Slovik—1974, Fear on Trial—1975, Escape From Iran: The Canadian Caper (CBS)—1981, Crisis at Central High (CBS)—1981

JORDON, Glenn
Agent: Creative Artists Agency
1888 Century Park East, Suite 1400
Los Angeles, CA 90067
Telephone: (213) 277-4545
credits: In the Matter of Karen Ann Quinlan (NBC), Sunshine Christmas (NBC), Les Miserables (CBS), Son-Rise (NBC), The Family Man (CBS), The Princess and the Cabbie (CBS)—1981, The Women's Room—1981

KAGAN, Jeremy Paul
(see also Motion Picture Directors)
Agent: Adams, Ray, and Rosenberg
Telephone: (213) 278-3000
credits: Unwed Father—1974, Katherine (ABC)—1975, Judge Dee, Scott Joplin—1976

KAPLAN, Jonathan
Bus. Mgr: Gerwin, Jamner & Pariser
Los Angeles, CA
Telephone: (213) 655-4410
credits: The 11th Victim (CBS)—1979, Muscle Beach (ABC)—1980, The Gentleman Bandit (CBS)—1981

KLEISER, Randal
(see also Motion Picture Directors)
Office: 3855 Lankershim Blvd.
North Hollywood, CA 91604
Telephone: (213) 760-3801
credits: All Together Now—1974, Dawn:

Portrait of a Teenage Runaway—1975, The Boy in the Plastic Bubble—1976, The Gathering—1977

KORTY, John
(see also Motion Picture Directors)
Agent: William Morris Agency
151 El Camino Drive
Beverly Hills, CA 90212
Telephone: (213) 274-7451
credits: The People—1972, Go Ask Alice (ABC)—1973, The Class of '63 (ABC)—1974, The Autobiography of Miss Jane Pittman (CBS)—1974, Farewell to Manzanar (NBC)—1976, Forever (CBS)—1977, A Christmas Without Snow (CBS)—1980

KRASNY, Paul
Agent: Shapiro-Lichtman, Inc.
2049 Century Park East
Los Angeles, CA 90067
Telephone: (213) 557-2244
credits: Terror Among Us (CBS), Fugitive Family (CBS), When Hell Was in Session (NBC), Centennial (NBC)—1979, Fly Away Home (ABC)—1981

LEACOCK, Philip
Agent: Contemporary-Korman Artists
132 Lasky Drive
Beverly Hills, CA 90212
Telephone: (213) 278-8250
credits: The Two Lives of Carol Letnes (CBS)—1981

LEE, Joanna
(see also Producers, Movies for TV(
Business: Christiana Productions
Columbia Pictures Television
Columbia Plaza
Burbank, CA 91505
Telephone: (213) 954-1844
credits: Mirror, Mirror (NBC), Children of Divorce (NBC), A Pocket Filled with Dreams—1975

directors, movies for television

LESTER, Mark
Agent: ICM
8899 Beverly Boulevard
Los Angeles, CA 90048
Telephone: (213) 550-4000

credits: Gold of the Amazon Women (NBC)—1978

LEVIN, Peter
Agent: Broder-Kurland Agency
9046 Sunset Boulevard
Los Angeles, CA 90069
Telephone: (213) 274-8921

credits: Rape in Marriage: The Rideout Case (CBS)—1979, The Comeback Kid (ABC)—1980, Palmerstown, U.S.A. (CBS)—1981, The Marva Collins Story (CBS)—1981, Washington Mistress (CBS)—1981

LEWIS, Robert
Agent: William Morris Agency
151 El Camino Drive
Beverly Hills, CA 90212
Telephone: (213) 274-7451

credits: Message to My Daughter, The Astronaut, Pray for the Wildcats, The Sam Sheppard Murder Case, Ring of Passion, If Things Were Different, S-H-E, Escape, Private Battle—1980, Brothers—1981, Fallen Angel (CBS)—1981, The Miracle of Kathy Miller (CBS)—1982, The Raid on Short Creek—1982, Desperate Lives (CBS)—1982

LIEBERMAN, Robert
Business: Harmony Pictures
2242 North Cahuenga Blvd.
Hollywood, CA 90068
Telephone: (213) 462-2121

credits: Fighting Back—The Story of Rocky Blier (ABC)—1980, Will—The Autobiography of G. Gordon Liddy (NBC)—1981

LONDON, Jerry
(see also Producers, Movies for TV)
Business: London Films
CBS Studio Center
4024 Radford Avenue
Studio City, CA 91604
Telephone: (213) 760-5000

Agent: Creative Artists Agency
1888 Century Park East, Suite 1400
Los Angeles, CA 90067
Telephone: (213) 277-4545

credits: World of Darkness, Swan Song, Women in White, Evening in Byzantium—1978, Wheels—1978, Shogun—1980, Father Figure—1981, The Ordeal of Bill Carney—1981, The Chicago Story—1981, The Gift of Life—1982

LOWRY, Dick M.
Agent: ICM
Business: PoKoJo Films
704 North Gardner Street
Los Angeles, CA 90046
Telephone: (213) 653-6115

credits: Jayne Mansfield (CBS), Kenny Rogers as The Gambler (CBS)—1980, The Pigs vs. the Freaks (NBC)—1980, Angel Dusted (NBC)—1980, Rascals and Robbers (CBS)—1981, Coward of the County (CBS)—1981, A Few Days in Weasel Creek (CBS)—1981, Where Are My Children (CBS)—1982, The Further Adventures of Tom Sawyer and Huckleberry Finn (CBS)—1982

MANN, Daniel
Agent: The Grossman-Stalmaster Agency
8730 Sunset Boulevard
Los Angeles, CA 90069
Telephone: (213) 657-3040

credits: Playing For Time (CBS)—1980, The Day the Loving Stopped—1981

MANN, Delbert
(see also Motion Picture Directors)
  Agent: William Morris Agency
  151 El Camino Drive
  Beverly Hills, CA 90212
  Telephone: (213) 274-7451
credits: Heidi (NBC)—1968, David Cop-
perfield (NBC)—1970, Jane Eyre (NBC)—
1971, She Waits (CBS)—1972, No Place
to Run (ABC)—1972, The Man Without a
Country (ABC)—1973, A Girl Named
Sooner (NBC)—1975, Francis Gary
Powers: The True Story of the U-2 Spy In-
cident (NBC)—1976, Tell Me My Name
(CBS)—1977, Breaking Up (ABC)—1978,
Home to Stay (CBS)—1978, Thou Shalt
Not Commit Adultery (NBC)—1978, Torn
Between Two Lovers (CBS)—1979, All
Quiet on the Western Front (CBS)—1979,
To Find My Son (CBS)—1980

MANN, Michael
(see also Motion Picture Directors)
  Agent: ICM
  8899 Beverly Boulevard
  Los Angeles, CA 90048
  Telephone: (213) 550-4000
  Business: Michael Mann Productions
  Zoetrope Studios
  1040 North Las Palmas
  Los Angeles, CA 90038
  Telephone: (213) 460-6133
credits: The Jericho Mile—1980

MARGOLIN, Stuart
  Bus. Manager: Bash, Gesas, & Co.
  Telephone: (213) 278-7700
credits: Suddenly Love—1979, The Long
Summer of George Adams—1981, A Shin-
ing Season (CBS)—1981

MARKOWITZ, Robert
  Agent: ICM

8899 Beverly Boulevard
Los Angeles, CA 90048
Telephone: (213) 550-4000
credits: The Wall (CBS)—The Deadliest
Season (CBS)—Storyteller (NBC)—Song
of Myself (CBS)—Pray TV (ABC)—1981

MARTINSON, Leslie H.
  Agent: Shapiro-Lichtman, Inc.
  2049 Century Park East, Suite 1320
  Los Angeles, CA 90067
  Telephone: (213) 557-2244
credits: Gilligan's Rescue (NBC)—1979,
The Kid with the Broken Halo (NBC)—
1981

MAYBERRY, Russel
  Agent: ICM
  8899 Beverly Boulevard
  Los Angeles, CA 90048
  Telephone: (213) 550-4000
credits: Probe, Side by Side: The Story of
the Osmond Family (NBC)—1981, A Matter of Life and Death, Reunion

MEDAK, Peter
(see also Motion Picture Directors)
  Agent: Agency for the Performing Arts
  9000 Sunset Blvd., Suite 315
  Los Angeles, CA 90069
  Telephone: (213) 273-0744
credits: Third Girl from the Left—1973,
The Babysitter—1980, Mistress of Para-
dise (ABC)—1981, The Dark Secret of
Black Bayou (ABC)—1981

McLAGLEN, Andrew V.
(see also Motion Picture Directors)
  Agent: Contemporary-Korman Artists
  132 Lasky Drive
  Beverly Hills, CA 90212
  Telephone: (213) 278-8250
credits: The Blue and the Gray (CBS miniseries)—1982

directors, movies for television

MEDFORD, Don
Agent: Irving Schechter, Inc.
404 North Roxbury Drive
Beverly Hills, CA 90210
Telephone: (213) 278-8070

credits: Coach of the Year, City of Angels—1977, The Man From Uncle, Sizzle (ABC)—1981

MICHAELS, Richard
Agent: Adams, Ray & Rosenberg
9200 Sunset Boulevard, Penthouse 25
Los Angeles, CA 90069
Telephone: (213) 278-3000

credits: Once An Eagle—1977, My Husband Is Missing—1978, Having Babies II—1978, Leave Yesterday Behind, Once Upon A Family, And Your Name Is Jonah—1979, The Plutonium Incident, Scared Straight: Another Story—1980, Berlin Tunnel 21—1981, The Butter Boys (CBS)—1981

MILLER, David
Agent: Phil Gersh Agency
222 North Canon Drive, Suite 201
Beverly Hills, CA 90210
Telephone: (213) 274-6611

credits: Goldie and the Boxer—1980, Goldie and the Boxer Go to Hollywood—1981

MILLER, Robert Ellis
Agent: The Paul Kohner Agency
9169 Sunset Boulevard
Los Angeles, CA 90069
Telephone: (213) 550-1060

credits: Just an Old Song—1976, Ishi, Last of His Tribe—1978, The Baltimore Bullet—1979, Madame X—1981

MOXEY, John Llewellyn
Personal Manager: Helen Kushnick

General Management Corp.
9100 Wilshire Boulevard
Beverly Hills, CA
Telephone: (213) 274-8805

credits: The Night Stalker—1973, The President's Mistress, Foster and Laurie, Nightmare in Badham County, Intimate Strangers, A Solitary Man, The Children of An Lac, The Violation of Sarah McDavid (CBS)—1981, Killjoy (CBS)—1981

NEUFELD, Sigmund, Jr.
Agent: Phil Rogers and Associates
9100 Sunset Boulevard, Suite 340
Los Angeles, CA 90069
Telephone: (213) 278-2015

credits: Me and Mr. Stenner (CBS)—1981

NOSSECK, Noel
(see also Motion Picture Directors)
Agent: Chasin-Park-Citron Agency
9255 Sunset Boulevard, Suite 915
Los Angeles, CA 90069
Telephone: (213) 273-7190

credits: Shadow of Fear, The Return of the Rebels (CBS)—1981

O'HERLIHY, Michael
Agent: Contemporary-Korman Artists, Ltd.
132 Lasky Drive
Beverly Hills, CA 90212
Telephone: (213) 278-8250

credits: The Last Voyage of the Valhalla—1980, I Married Wyatt Earp—1981, The Million Dollar Face (NBC)—1981

O'STEEN, Sam
Bus. Manager: Robert Morgan
Los Angeles, CA
Telephone: (213) 274-0891

O'STEEN, Sam, *continued*

credits: Queen of the Stardust Ballroom—1975, A Brand New Life—1976, I Love You, Goodbye—1977, High Risk—1978, The Best Little Girl in the World (ABC)—1981

PAGE, Anthony
Agent: Rhonda Gomez
Adams, Ray & Rosenberg
9200 Sunset Blvd.
Los Angeles, CA 90069
Telephone: (213) 278-3000

credits: Pueblo, Missiles of October, Fitzgerald in Hollywood, The Patricia Neal Story *(with Anthony Harvey)* (CBS)—1981, Bill (CBS)—1981

PETRIE, Daniel
(see also Motion Picture Directors)
Agent: ICM
8899 Beverly Boulevard
Los Angeles, CA 90048
Telephone: (213) 550-4000

credits (television only): Moon of the Wolf—1972, Mousy—1973, Trouble Comes to Town—1973, The Gun and the Pulpit—1974, Sybil—1976, Eleanor and Franklin—1976, Eleanor and Franklin–The White House Years—1977, Silent Night, Lonely Night—1977

PHILIPS, Lee
Agent: Shapiro-Lichtman
2049 Century Park East, Suite 1320
Los Angeles, CA 90067
Telephone: (213) 557-2244

credits: Valentine, The Special Olympics, Red Badge of Courage, The War Between the Tates, Louis Armstrong–Chicago Style, The Girl Most Likely To...—1974, Sweet Hostage, Crazy Times—1981

POST, Ted
(see also Motion Picture Directors)
Business: T.P. Films Ltd.
3250 Ocean Park Boulevard
Santa Monica, CA
Telephone: (213) 452-7747

credits: Dr. Cook's Garden—1975, Do Not Fold, Spindle, or Mutilate, Girls in the Office, Cagney & Lacey—1981

PRESSMAN, Michael
(see also Motion Picture Directors)
Agent: Creative Artists Agency
1888 Century Park East, Suite 1400
Los Angeles, CA 90067
Telephone: (213) 277-4545

credits: Like Mom, Like Me—1978

REISNER, Allen
Agent: Chasin-Park-Citron
9255 Sunset Boulevard
Los Angeles, CA 90069
Telephone: (213) 273-7190

credits: The Captains and the Kings—1977, To Die in Paris—1978, The Cliff, Cops and Robin, Skag—1980

RICH, David Lowell
Agent: Jack Gilardi, ICM
8899 Beverly Boulevard
Los Angeles, CA 90048
Telephone: (213) 550-4000

credits: Horror at 37,000 Feet, Telethon, SST Death Flight, David the King, See How They Run, Death Race, Runaway!, Berlin Affair, The Secret Life of John Chapman, Lt. Shuster's Wife, Enola Gay, The Borgia Stick, A Family Upside Down, The Defection of Sima Kudirka, Thursday's Child (CBS)—1982

SARAFIAN, Richard C.
Agent: Agency for the Performing Arts
9000 Sunset Boulevard, Suite 315
Los Angeles, CA 90069
Telephone: (213) 273-0744
credits: Splendor in the Grass (NBC)—1981

SARGENT, Joseph
(see also Motion Picture Directors)
Business: Joseph Sargent Productions
Metromedia Producers Corp.
5746 Sunset Boulevard
Hollywood, CA 90028
Telephone: (213) 462-7111
credits: Tribes (ABC)—1969, Maybe I'll Come Home in the Spring (ABC)—1970, The Marcus Nelson Murders (CBS)—1973, Sunshine (CBS)—1973, Hustling (ABC)—1975, Friendly Persuasion (ABC)—1975, The Night that Panicked America (ABC)—1975, Amber Waves (ABC)—1980, The Manions of America (ABC)—1981, Tomorrow's Child (ABC)—1982

SATLOF, Ron
(see also Motion Picture Directors)
Business: Metaphor Productions
155 North La Peer Drive
Los Angeles, CA 90048
Telephone: (213) 278-2351
credits: From Here to Eternity—1979

SCHAEFER, George
Business: Schaefer-Karpf Productions
Warners Hollywood Studios
1041 North Formosa Avenue
Los Angeles, CA 90046
Telephone: (213) 650-2500
credits: Scott Fitzgerald and the Last of the Belles, Blind Ambition—1979, First You Cry—1979, The People vs. Jean Harris—1981, The Bunker—1981, A Piano for Mrs. Cimino—1981, The Deadly Game (cable-tv film)—1982

SHAVELSON, Melville
Business: Llenroc Productions, Inc.
1801 Avenue of the Stars, Suite 911
Los Angeles, CA 90067
Telephone: (213) 67
credits: The Legend of Valentino—1975, The Great Houdinis, Ike—1978

STERN, Steven Hillard
Agent: ICM
8899 Beverly Boulevard
Los Angeles, CA 90048
Telephone: (213) 550-4000
credits: Escape from Bogen Country—1980, Ghost of Flight 401, Getting Married—1978, Fast Friends, Miracle on Ice (ABC)—1981, A Small Killing—1981, The Ambush Murders (CBS)—1982, An American Love Affair (CBS)—1982

SWACKHAMER, E. W.
Agent: Shapiro-Lichtman
2049 Century Park East, Suite 1320
Los Angeles, CA 90067
Telephone: (213) 557-2244
credits: The Oklahoma City Girls (ABC)—1981

TAYLOR, Don
(see also Motion Picture Directors)
Agent: Phil Gersh Agency
222 North Canon Drive, Suite 201
Beverly Hills, CA 90210
Telephone: (213) 274-6611
credits: The Red Flag—1981, Broken Promise—1981

TAYLOR, Jud
Agent: Creative Artists Agency
1888 Century Park East, Suite 1400
Los Angeles, CA 90067
Telephone: (213) 277-4545

TAYLOR, Jud, *continued*

credits: Tail Gunner Joe—1978, Man of Honor—1981, Act of Love, Flesh and Blood, Lovey—Circle of Children II

TEWKESBURY, Joan
(see also Screenwriters)
 Agent: ICM
 8899 Beverly Boulevard
 Los Angeles, CA 90048
 Telephone: (213) 550-4000

credits: The Acorn People—1980, The Tenth Month—1981

VOGEL, Virgil
 Agent: David Shapira & Associates
 9100 Wilshire Boulevard
 Suite 231, East Tower
 Beverly Hills, CA 90212
 Telephone: (213) 278-2742

credits: Centennial—1979

WANAMAKER, Sam
 Business: S. W. Productions, Ltd.
 9100 Wilshire Boulevard, Suite 500
 Beverly Hills, CA 90212
 Telephone: (213) 273-2782
 Agent: William Morris Agency

credits: The Dark Side of Love, The Killing of Randy Webster (CBS)—1981

WENDKOS, Paul
 Agent: Creative Artists Agency
 1888 Century Park East, Suite 1400
 Los Angeles, CA 90067
 Telephone: (213) 277-4545

credits: A Death of Innocence, The Woman I Love, The Legend of Lizzie Borden—1975, 79 Park Avenue—1979, A Woman Called Moses, Betrayal, The Five of Me—1981

WERNER, Peter

 Agent: Robert Stein
 The Paul Kohner Agency
 9169 Sunset Boulevard
 Los Angeles, CA 90069
 Telephone: (213) 550-1060

credits: Battered (NBC)—1978, Aunt Mary (CBS)—1980

WIARD, William O.
 Agent: Adams, Ray & Rosenberg
 9200 Sunset Blvd., Penthouse 25
 Los Angeles, CA 90069
 Telephone: (213) 278-3000

credits: This House Is Possessed (ABC)—1981, Fantasies (ABC)—1981

WISE, Herbert
 Personal Manager: Tim Corrie
 Fraser & Dunlop, Ltd.
 London, England
 Telephone: 01-734-7311

credits: Skokie (CBS)—1981

WYRE, Donald

credits: Divorce Wars: A Love Story (ABC)—1982

YOUNG, Roger
 Agent: Broder-Kurland Agency
 9046 Sunset Boulevard
 Los Angeles, CA 90069
 Telephone: (213) 274-8921

credits: Bitter Harvest—1981, One Starry Night (CBS)—1981

ZEFFIRELLI, Franco
(see also Motion Picture Directors)
 Agent: Stan Kamen
 William Morris Agency
 151 El Camino Drive
 Beverly Hills, CA 90212
 Telephone: (213) 274-7451

credits: Jesus of Nazareth—1976

PRODUCERS
MOVIES FOR TELEVISION

ABRAMS, Gerald W.

Business: Cypress Point Productions
3910 Overland Avenue
Culver City, CA 90230
Telephone: (213) 202-4272

credits: The Defection of Simas Kudirka, The Secret Life of John Chapman, Secrets, Hollywood High; *(as Executive Producer):* James Dean–Portrait of a Friend, Having Babies, Having Babies II and III, Red Alert, Ski Lift to Death, Murder at the Mardi Gras, With This Ring, Flesh and Blood, letters from Frank, The Gift, Steeltown, Act of Love, Berlin Tunnel 21, Marian Rose White—1982

ALLEN, Irwin

(see also Motion Picture Producers)
Business: Irwin Allen Productions
Columbia Plaza
Burbank, CA 91505
Telephone: (213) 954-4000

credits: Flood—1976, Fire—1977, The Return of Captain Nemo—1977, Hanging by a Thread—1978, The Memory of Eva Ryker—1980, Code Red (ABC)—1981

AVNET, Jon

Business: Tisch/Avnet Productions
515 North Robertson Boulevard
Los Angeles, CA 90048
Telephone: (213) 278-7680

credits: No Other Love (CBS)—1979, Homeward Bound (CBS)—1980, Prime Suspect (CBS)—1982, Big Brother (CBS)—1983 *(all are co-productions with Steve Tisch)*

BAER, Bob

credits: Genesis (ABC)—1981

BANNER, Bob

Business: Bob Banner Associates, Inc.
8687 Melrose Ave., Suite M-20
Los Angeles, CA 90069
Telephone: (213) 657-6800

credits: My Sweet Charlie—1970, Lisa Bright and Dark—1974, Journey from Darkness—1975, My Husband Is Missing—1978, Bud & Lou—1979, If Things Were Different—1979

BARKLEY, Deanne

Business: The Belle Company
15301 Ventura Blvd., Suite 230
Sherman Oaks, CA 91403
Telephone: (213) 907-1450

credits: The Ordeal of Bill Carney *(as Executive Producer)* (CBS)—1981, Side by Side, The Story of the Osmond Family (NBC)—1982

BASS, Jules and
RANKIN, Arthur

Business: Rankin/Bass Prod.
1 East 53rd Street
New York, NY 10022
Telephone: (212) 759-7721

credits: Dorian's Portrait—1981, The Geisha (ABC)—[upcoming]

BENSON, Hugh

credits: Goliath Awaits (OPT)—1981, The Blue and the Gray (Co-prod. with Harry Thomason (CBS)—1982

BERCOVICI, Eric

Office: MGM Studios
10202 West Washington Boulevard
Culver City, CA 90230
Telephone: (213) 558-5000

credits: Shogun—1980, The Chicago Story *(exec. prod.)* (NBC)—1981

BERGER, Robert and
BRODKIN, Herbert
    Business: Titus Productions
    211 East 51st Street
    New York, NY 10022
    Telephone: (212) 752-6460

credits: Pueblo, The Missiles of October, Holocaust—1978, Skokie—1981

BINDER, Steve
    Business: Steve Binder Productions
    666 North Robertson
    Los Angeles, CA 90069
    Telephone: (213) 652-4422

credits: An Innocent Love (CBS)—1981, One Starry Night *(exec. prod.)*—1981

BLASDEL-GODDARD, Audrey
credits: Fallen Angel (ABC)—1981

BREGMAN, Buddy
    Office: Columbia Pictures Television
    300 Colgems Square
    Burbank, CA 91522
    Telephone: (213) 954-6000

credits: The Carmen Miranda Story—[upcoming], Bing—[upcoming]

BRODKIN, Herbert and
BERGER, Robert
    Business: Titus Productions
    211 East 51st Street
    New York, NY 10022
    Telephone: (212) 752-6460

credits: Pueblo, The Missiles of October, Holocaust—1978, Skokie—1981, My Body, My Child (ABC) *(as Executive Producer)*—1982

CANNELL, Stephen J.
    Business: Stephen J. Cannell
    Productions
    5555 Melrose Avenue
    Los Angeles, CA 90038
    Telephone: (213) 465-5800

credits: The Witching *(as Executive Producer)* (ABC)—1981

CLARK, Dick
    Business: Dick Clark Cinema Prod.
    3003 West Olive Avenue
    Burbank, CA 91505
    Telephone: (213) 841-3003

credits: Elvis—1980, The Birth of the Beatles, The Man in the Santa Claus Suit, Murder in Texas *(as Executive Producer)*—1981

CLARK, Susan
    Business: Georgian Bay Productions
    3620 Fredonia Drive, No. 1
    Hollywood, CA 90068
    Telephone: (213) 851-8771

credits: Jimmy B. and Andre (CBS)—1979, Word of Honor *(as Executive Producer and Producer)* (CBS)—1980, Maid in America *(as Executive Producer)* (CBS)—1982

CATES, Gilbert
    Business: The Cates Bros. Co.
    9200 Sunset Boulevard, Suite 913
    Los Angeles, CA 90069
    Telephone: (213) 273-7773

credits: The Kid from Nowhere—1981

COTTLE, Anna
    Office: Warner Bros. TV
    4000 Warner Boulevard
    Burbank, CA 91522
    Telephone: (213) 954-6000

credits: The Letter—1981

producers, movies for television

CRAMER, Douglas
Business: Aaron Spelling Productions
Warner Hollywood Studios
1041 North Formosa Avenue
Los Angeles, CA 90046
Telephone: (213) 650-2661

credits: Sizzle *(as Co-executive Producer)*
(ABC)—1981

CURTIS, Dan
(see also Directors, Movies for TV)
Office: Paramount Television
5555 Melrose Avenue
Los Angeles, CA 90038
Telephone: (213) 465-5800

credits: The Last Ride of the Dalton Gang
(NBC)—1979, Mrs. R's Daughter (NBC)—
1979, The Long Days of Summer (ABC)—
1980, I Think I'm Having a Baby—1980,
The Winds of War (ABC miniseries)—1982

DEBIN, David
Business: Debin-Locke Co.
1119 North McCadden Place
Hollywood, CA 90038
Telephone: (213) 462-2608

credits: A Gun in the House *(co-prod. with
Peter Locke)* (CBS)—1981, The Star
Maker *(co-prod. with Peter Locke)*
(NBC)—1981

ECKSTEIN, George
Office: Warner Bros. TV
4000 Warner Boulevard
Burbank, CA 91522
Telephone: (213) 954-6543

credits: Duel—1971, Banacek—1972,
Sunshine—1973, Emelia Earhart—1974,
Tail Gunner Joe—1975, Christmas Sun-
shine—1977, 79 Park Ave.—1978,
Masada—1981, Sidney Shorr—1981, The
Letter *(as exec. prod.)*—1981, In Our
Hands *(as exec. prod.)*—1981

FELLOWS, Arthur
Business: The Fellows/Keegan
Lorimar Productions
3970 Overland Avenue
Culver City, CA 90230
Telephone: (213) 202-2279

*credits (all are co-productions with Terry
Keegan):* The Top of the Hill (miniseries)—
1978, The Girl, the Gold Watch and Dyna-
mite *(co-Executive Producer)*—1980, The
Girl, the Gold Watch, and Everything *(co-
Executive Producer))*—1980, Desperate
Lives (CBS)—1981, So Little Cause for
Caroline (CBS)—1982

FINNEGAN, Bill
FINNEGAN, Pat
Business: Finnegan Associates
4225 Coldwater Canyon
Studio City, CA 91604
Telephone: (213) 985-0430

credits: Between Two Brothers
(CBS)—1981, World War III (NBC)—1981,
Dangerous Company (CBS)—1981

FOREMAN, Carl
(see also Motion Picture Producers)
Business: High Noon Productions
100 Universal City Plaza
Universal City, CA 91608
Telephone: (213) 508-3117

credits: The Brownsville Raid—[upcom-
ing]

FRIENDLY, Ed
Business: Ed Friendly Productions
1041 North Formosa
Los Angeles, CA 90046
Telephone: (213) 650-2475

credits: Little House on the Prairie—1974,
Young Pioneers—1976, Young Pioneers
Christmas—1976, Peter Lundy and the
Medicine Hat Stallion—1977, Backstairs

at the Whitehouse (miniseries)—1979, The Flame Is Love—1980, Judgement Day—1981

FRIES, Charles
Business: Charles Fries Productions
4024 Radford Avenue
Studio City, CA 91604
Telephone: (213) 760-5000

credits: The Martian Chronicles (NBC)—1978, Leave 'Em Laughing—1981, Bitter Harvest *(exec. prod.)* (NBC)—1981, Ambush Murders *(exec. prod.)* (CBS)—1981, Twirl *(exec. prod.)* (NBC)—1981

GANZ, Tony
Office: Major H Productions
5555 Melrose Avenue
Los Angeles, CA 90038
Telephone: (213) 468-5000

credits: Bitter Harvest (NBC)—1981 *(Vice President of Creative Affairs)*

GERBER, David
Business: David Gerber Productions
10202 West Washington Blvd.
Culver City, CA 90230
Telephone: (213) 558-6400

credits: The Night the City Screamed—1980, Beaulah Land—1980, Elvis and the Beauty Queen—1981, Terror Among Us—1981, Cry for the Stranger (CBS)—1982

GIMBEL, Roger
Business: EMI Television Programs
9229 Sunset Blvd.—9th Floor
Los Angeles, CA 90069
Telephone: (213) 859-8250

credits: The Autobiography of Miss Jane Pittman—1974, Queen of the Stardust Ballroom—1975, The Amazing Howard Hughes—1977, The Glass House—1978, Sophia Loren, Her Own Story—1980, My Kidnapper, My Love (NBC)—1980,Manions of America (ABC)—1981, Broken Promise (CBS)—1981, A Piano for Mrs. Cimino—1981, The Killing of Randy Webster *(with Tony Converse)*—1981, Maria Callas *(with Tony Converse)*—1981, Man of Honor *(with Tony Converse)* (CBS)—1981, Report to Murphy (CBS)—1981, A Question of Honor (CBS)—1982

GLICKMAN, Joel
credits: Night Terror, Angel on Horseback

GOLDSMITH, David
credits: The Ambush Murders (CBS)—1982

GOWANS, Kip
Office: Warner Bros. TV
4000 Warner Boulevard
Burbank, CA 91522
Telephone: (213) 954-6000

credits: The Women's Room—1980, The Letter—1981

GREEN, James
Business: Green/Epstein Productions
100 Universal City Plaza, Bldg. 507
Suite 4-D
Universal City, CA 91608
Telephone: (213) 508-3112

credits: Fast Friends—1979, Women at West Point—1979, Breaking Up Is Hard To Do—1979, A Shining Season—1979, To Find My Son—1980, Fallen Angel (ABC)—1981, Money on the Side (ABC)—1982

GREENBERG, Peter S.
Office: ABC Circle Films

producers, movies for television

9911 West Pico Boulevard
Los Angeles, CA 90035
Telephone: (213) 557-6837

credits: Can You Hear the Laughter (CBS)—1978, Pray TV (ABC)—1981, Red Flag (CBS)—1981

GROSSO, Sonny
Business: Grosso Jacobson Prod.
330 East 80th Street
New York, NY 10019
Telephone: (212) 744-4893

credits: Man of Honor—1981, False Witness—[upcoming]

HAGEN, Ross
Business: The Movie Outfit
20964 Almazan Road
Woodland Hills, CA 91364
Telephone: (213) 992-4714

credits: The Wonderful World of Stunts

HALE, Billy
Business: Billy Hale Films

credits: Murder in Texas—1981

HAMNER, Robert
Business: Nephi/Hamner Productions

credits (as exec. prod.): The Million Dollar Face *(with Robert D. Wood)*—1981, Malibu—1981, The J. R. Richard Story—[upcoming], Mickey Spillane's Mike Hammer (CBS)—1981, Portrait of a Showgirl (CBS)—1982

HILL, Len
Business: Hill/Mandelker Films, Inc.
Twentiety Century-Fox Studios
10201 West Pico Boulevard
Los Angeles, CA 90035
Telephone: (213) 277-2211

credits: Dream House—1981, Mae West—1982

HOUGH, Stan
Office: CBS Television
4024 Radford Avenue
Studio City, CA 91604
Telephone: (213) 760-5000

credits: Mrs. Sundance—1976, The Sundance Woman—1977, Scott Joplin, Walking through the Fire (CBS)—1979, Peter and Paul—1981

JACKS, Robert L.
Office: Warner Bros. Television
4000 Warner Boulevard
Burbank, CA 91522
Telephone: (213) 954-3041

credits: A Few Days in Weasel Creek (CBS)—1981

JARVIS, Lucy
Business: Creative Concepts, Inc.
45 Rockerfeller Plaza, Room 715
New York, NY 10111
Telephone (212) 541-7776

credits: Family Reunion (NBC)—1981

KATZ, Peter
Office: CBS Studio Center
4024 Radford Avenue
Studio City, CA 91604
Telephone: (213) 760-5769
Agent: FCA Agency, Inc.
Telephone: (213) 277-8422

credits: Gibbsville (NBC)—1975, Kill Me If You Can (NBC)—1976, Murder in Peyton Place (NBC)—1977, A Question of Guilt (CBS)—1981, A Man Called Intrepid (NBC miniseries)—1979, Sophia, Living and Loving (NBC)—1980, The Acorn People (NBC)—1980, Dial M for Murder (NBC)—1981, Patricia Neal Story (English segment)—1981, Million Dollar Infield (CBS)—1981, Thursday's Child (CBS)—1982

KATZKA, Gabriel
Business: Pantheon TV Productions
545 Madison Avenue
New York, NY 10019
Telephone: (212) 832-6650

credits: A Life of Her Own—1981, Lady in a Corner—[upcoming], Love of Ireland—[upcoming], Ellis Island—[upcoming]

KAYDEN, William
Business: Wm. Kayden Productions
4000 Warner Boulevard
Burbank, CA 91522
Telephone: (213) 954-3183

credits: I Heard the Owl Call My Name—1973, The Family Nobody Wanted (ABC)—1976, Cops and Robin (NBC)—1978, Yesterday's Child (NBC)—1978, Lady of the House (NBC)—1979, Crazy Times (ABC)—1981, Where Are My Children (CBS)—1983

KEEGAN, Terry
Business: Fellows/Keegan
3970 Overland Avenue
Culver City, CA 90230
Telephone: (213) 202-2281

credits (all are co-productions with Arthur Fellows): The Top of the Hill (miniseries)—1978, The Girl, the Gold Watch, and Dynamite (OPT) (co-executive Producer)—1980, Desperate Lives (CBS)—1981, So Little Cause for Caroline (CBS)—1982

KELLER, Max and Micheline
Business: Inter Planetary Productions
14555 Ventura Blvd.
Sherman Oaks, CA 91423
Telephone: (213) 981-4950

credits: Strangers in Our House (as Executive Producers) (NBC)—1978, Grambling's White Tiger (co-Executive Producers) (NBC)—1981, Kent State (co-produced with Philip Barry) (NBC)—1981, The First Amendment Story (CBS)—1983

KLEIN, Paul
Business: PKO-TV
32 East 57th Street
New York, NY 10022
Telephone: (212) 888-1770

credits: 300 Miles for Stephanie (exec. prod.)—1980, The People vs. Jean Harris (NBC)—1981, A Gun in the House (exec. prod.)—1981

KONIGSBERG, Frank
Business: The Konigsberg Company
10201 West Pico Boulevard
Los Angeles, CA 90064
Telephone: (213) 203-3144

credits: Bing Crosby, His Life and Legend—1978, Pearl (miniseries)—1978, Dummy—1979, Before and After—1979, The Guyana Tragedy—1980, A Christmas without Snow—1980, The Pride of Jesse Hallam—1981, Divorce Wars (ABC)—1982, Coming Out of the Ice (CBS)—1982

KRAGEN, Ken
Business: Kragen & Co.
1112 North Sherbourne Drive
Los Angeles, CA 90069
Telephone: (213) 854-4400

credits: Kenny Rogers as The Gambler—1980, Coward of the County—1981

KROFFT, Sid and
KROFFT, Marty
Business: Krofft Entertainment, Inc.
7200 Vineland Avenue
Sun Valley, CA 91352
Telephone: (213) 875-3250

credits: Side Show (NBC)—1981

KROST, Barry
   Business: The Movie Company
   336 North Foothill Road
   Beverly Hills, CA 90210
   Telephone: (213) 271-7254

credits: The Rules of Marriage (as Executive Producer) (CBS)—1982

LABELLA, Vincenzo
   Agent: John Mitchell
   1801 Avenue of the Stars
   Century City, CA 90067

credits: Jesus of Nazareth—1975, Marco Polo (NBC)—1982

LANDSBURG, Alan
   Business: Alan Landsburg Productions
   1554 South Sepulveda
   Los Angeles, CA 90025
   Telephone: (213) 473-9641

credits: Bill—1981, Me and Mr. Stenner (as exec. prod.)—1981

LEE, Joanna
(see also Directors, Movies for TV)
   Business: Christiana Productions
   Columbia Studios
   Burbank, CA 91522
   Telephone: (213) 954-1844

credits: I Want to Keep My Baby (CBS)—1977, Mary Jane Harper Cried Last Night, Like Normal People (ABC)—1979, Mirror, Mirror (NBC), Love Tapes, Children of Divorce (NBC)—1981

LEIDER, Jerry
(see also Motion Picture Producers)
   Business: Jerry Leider Productions
   Warner Hollywood Studios
   10401 North Formosa Avenue
   Los Angeles, CA 90046
   Telephone: (213) 650-2888

credits: The Hostage Tower—1980, Willa—1979, And I Alone Survived—1978

**LEVENBACK, Paula and
RICHE, Wendy**
   Business: Levenback/Riche
      Productions
   100 Universal Plaza
   Universal City, CA 91608
   Telephone: (213) 508-2645

credits: Madame X—1981

LEVY, Franklin
(see also Motion Picture Producers)
   Business: Catalina Productions
   4000 Warner Blvd.
   Burbank, CA 91522
   Telephone: (213) 954-6447

credits: The Last Hurrah (co-produced) (NBC), Return Engagement (NBC), Enola Gay (Executive Producer with Mike Wise and Richard Reisberg) (NBC)—1980, The Day the Buble Burst (co-Executive Producer) (NBC), The Child Stealer (co-Executive Producer) (ABC), For Ladies Only (with Gregory Harrison) (NBC)—1982

LOCKE, Peter
   Business: Debin-Locke Co.
   1119 North McCadden Place
   Hollywood, CA 90038
   Telephone: (213) 462-2608

credits (with David Debin): A Gun in the House (CBS)—1981, The Star Maker (NBC)—1981

LONDON, Jerry
(see also Motion Picture Directors)
   Business: London Films, Inc.
   4024 Radford Avenue
   Studio City, CA 91604
   Telephone: (213) 760-5000

credits: The Ordeal of Bill Carney—1981, The Gift of Life—1982

LORING, Lynn
Aaron Spelling Productions
1041 North Formosa Avenue
Los Angeles, CA 90046
Telephone: (213) 650-2500

credits: Sizzle *(with Cindy Dunne)*—1981, The Best Little Girl in the World—1981

MANDELKER, Philip
Business: Hill/Mandelker Films, Inc.
Twentieth Century-Fox Studios
10201 West Pico Boulevard
Los Angeles, CA 90035
Telephone: (213) 277-2211

credits: Amber Waves (ABC)—1980, The Women's Room (ABC)—1980, Freedom (ABC)—1981, Dream House *(co-Executive Producer with Len Hill)*—1981, Mae West *(with Len Hill)*—1982

MANSON, David

credits: A Rumor of War (CBS)—1980, A Love Story: Eleanor and Lou Gehrig—1981

MARGULIES, Stan
Business: The Stan Margulies Co.
4000 Warner Boulevard
Burbank, CA 91522
Telephone: (213) 954-2166

credits: Roots—1976, Roots: The Next Generations—1978, Moviola (NBC)—1980, Murder Is Easy—1981, The Thorn Birds (miniseries)—1982

McNEELY, Jerry
Office: Twentieth Century-Fox TV
10201 West Pico Boulevard
Los Angeles, CA 90064
Telephone: (213) 277-2211

credits: Lucas Tanner, Three for the Road, Something for Joey, The Critical List *(as Executive Product)*, The Boy Who Drank Too Much *(Executive Producer)*, Fighting Back: The story of Rocky Bleier *(Executive Producer)*, Tomorrow's Child *(as Executive Producer)*—1981

NELSON, Peter and
ORGOLINI, Arnold
Business: Orgolini-Nelson Productions
9336 West Washington Boulevard
Culver City, CA 90230
Telephone: (213) 836-5537

credits: The Last Song—1980, A Small Killing (CBS)—1981, Callie and Son—1981, Starflight 1 (ABC)—1982

NEUFELD, Mace
Business: Neufeld-Davis Productions
9454 Wilshire Boulevard, Suite 309
Beverly Hills, CA 90212
Telephone: (213) 858-2929

credits: Angel on my Shoulder—1980, American Dream—1981, Cagney & Lacey—1981, East of Eden *(exec. prod.)*—1981

NEUMAN, E. Jack
Contact: ABC Circle Films
9911 West Pico Boulevard
Los Angeles, CA 90035
Telephone: (213) 557-6853

credits: Inside the Third Reich (ABC)—1981

NEWLAND, John
Business: The Factor-Newland
Production Co.
4000 Warner Blvd.
Burbank, CA 91522
Telephone: (213) 954-1701

credits (as executive producers): A Sensitive, Passionate Man, Overboard—1980, The Suicide's Wife, Angel City, The Five of Me—1981

producers, movies for television

ORGOLINI, Arnold and
NELSON, Peter
  Business: Orgolini-Nelson Productions
  9336 West Washington Boulevard
  Culver City, CA 90230
  Telephone: (213) 836-5537
credits: The Last Song—1980, A Small
Killing (CBS)—1981, Callie and Son—
1981, Starflight 1—1982

PAPAZIAN, Robert
  Business: Robert Papazian Prod.
  Telephone: (213) 508-5533
credits: The Two Lives of Carol Letner
(CBS)—1981, Stand By Your Man—1981,
Dial 911 (CBS)—1981

POMPIAN, Paul
  Paul Pompian Productions
  10202 West Washington Blvd.
  Culver City, CA 90230
  Telephone: (213) 558-5000
credits: Death of a Centerfold: The
Dorothy Stratton Story (NBC)—1981,
Hear No Evil (CBS)—1982, The Shah of
Iran (NBC)—[upcoming]

RANKIN, Arthur and
BASS, Jules
  Business: Rankin/Bass Productions
  1 East 53rd Street
  New York, NY 10022
  Telephone (212) 759-7721
credits: Dorian's Portrait—1981, The
Geisha (ABC)—[upcoming]

RANSOHOFF, Martin
  Business: Martin Ransohoff Productions
  300 Colgems Square
  Burbank, CA 91522
  Telephone: (213) 954-3491
credits: Lazarus (CBS)—1983

REDA, Lou
  Business: Lou Reda Productions
  44 North Second Street
  Easton, PA 18042
  Telephone: (215) 258-2957
credits: The Blue and the Gray (Executive
Producer with Larry White) (CBS)—1982

RICHE, Wendy and
LEVENBACK, Paula
  Business: Levenback/Riche Prod.
  100 Universal Plaza
  Universal City, CA 91608
  Telephone: (213) 508-2645
credits: Madame X—1981

RISSIEN, Eddie
  Business: Playboy Productions
  8560 Sunset Blvd.
  Los Angeles, CA 90069
  Telephone: (213) 659-4080
credits: Third Girl from the Left—1972, A
Summer Without Boys—1973, The Great
Niagara—1974, Shadow in the Streets—
1975, Beyond the Bermuda Triangle—
1975, Minstrel Man—1977, The Death of
Ocean Park—1979, A Whale for the Kill-
ing (as exec. prod.)—1981

ROSEMONT, Norman
  Business: Norman Rosemont
         Productions
  9808 Wilshire Blvd., Suite 304
  Beverly Hills, CA 90212
  Telephone: (213) 550-8130
credits: Ivanhoe (CBS)—1982

ROSENBERG, Meta
  Business: Warner Bros. TV
  4000 Warner Boulevard
  Burbank, CA 91522
credits: Hangin' On (as exec. prod.)—
1981

ROSENZWEIG, Barney
    Contact: Paramount Pictures
    5555 Melrose Avenue
    Los Angeles, CA 90038
    Telephone: (213) 468-5000

credits: Angel on My Shoulder—1980, Cagney and Lacey—1981, American Dream—1981, East of Eden—1981

RUDOLPH, Louis
    Office: Columbia Pictures Television
    Columbia Plaza
    Burbank, CA 91505
    Telephone: (213) 954-2668

credits: A Case of Rape—1979, The Sam Shepperd Story—1980, Jacqueline Bouvier Kennedy—1981, Ike (miniseries) (ABC)—1979, Attica (ABC)—1980

SACKS, Alan
    Business: Alan Sacks Productions
    12007 Guerin Street
    Studio City, CA 91604
    Telephone: (213) 980-8816

credits: Women at West Point, Cry For Love, Murder, Inc., The Family Kovac, Leave 'Em Laughing *(as supervising producer)*—1981, Twirl (NBC)—1981, Rosie–The Rosemary Clooney Story *(as Supervising Producer)*—1982

SAMUELS, Ronald I.
    Business: Ron Samuels Prod., Inc.
    9720 Wilshire Blvd., Suite 506
    Beverly Hills, CA 90212
    Telephone: (213) 273-8964

credits (as executive producer): The Last Song (CBS), The Two Worlds of Jennie Logan *(with Joe Wizan)* (CBS), Callie and Son (CBS), Scruples (miniseries) (CBS), The Incredible Journey of Dr. Meg Laurel (CBS), Born to be Sold (NBC)—1981, Mill River (CBS), Reachout (CBS)

SILLIPHANT, Stirling
(see also Screenwriters)
    Business: Pingree Company
    4000 Warner Boulevard
    Burbank, CA 91522
    Telephone: (213) 954-1385

credits: The First 36 Hours of Dr. Durant, Pearl *(as Executive Producer)* (miniseries)—1978, Salem's Lot *(as Executive Producer)*, Fly Away Home (ABC)—1981

SIMPSON, O. J.
    Business: Orenthal Productions
    Burbank Studios
    4000 Warner Boulevard
    Burbank, CA 91522
    Telephone: (213) 954-6000

credits (as exec. prod.): Detour to Terror—1980, Goldie and the Boxer—1980, Goldie and the Boxer Go to Hollywood (NBC)—1981, Cocaine and Blue Eyes *(co-produced with Dan Mark)* (NBC)—1983

SINGER, Robert
    Business: Blatt-Singer Productions
    4000 Warner Boulevard
    Burbank, CA 91522
    Telephone: (213) 954-2631

credits: The Children Nobody Wanted (CBS)—1981, Independence Day *(co-produced with Dan Blatt)*—1982

SPELLING, Aaron
    Business: Aaron Spelling Productions
    Warner's Hollywood Studios
    1041 North Formosa Avenue
    Los Angeles, CA 90048
    Telephone: (213) 650-3391

credits (as exec. prod.): The Legend of Valentino—1975, The Boy in the Plastic Bubble—1976, One of My Wives is Missing—1976, Little Ladies of the Night—1977, The Users—1978, Murder Can Hurt You—

producers, movies for television

1980, The Best Little Girl in the World—1981, Sizzle—1981, Matt Houston—1982, Maserati and the Brain—1982

Aaron Spelling has executive produced over 90 movies for television

STRANGIS, Greg
   Business: Ten-Four Productions
   8271 Melrose Avenue
   Los Angeles, CA 90046

credits: An American Love Affair (CBS)—1982

STRANGIS, Sam
   Business: Ten-Four Productions
   8271 Melrose Avenue
   Los Angeles, CA 90046
   Telephone: (213) 655-9470

credits: Rainbow (NBC)—1978, Better Late Than Never (NBC)—1978, The Great American Traffic Jam (NBC)—1980, The Pigs Vs. The Freaks—1980, Rivkin: Bounty Hunter (CBS)—1981, An American Love Affair *(as Executive Producer)* (CBS)—1982

TISCH, Steve
(see also Motion Picture Producers)
   Tisch/Avnet Productions
   515 North Robertson Boulevard
   Los Angeles, CA 90048
   Telephone: (213) 278-7680

credits (all are co-productions with Jon Avnet): No Other Love (CBS)—1979, Homeward Bound (CBS)—1980, Prime Suspect (CBS)—1982, Big Brother (CBS)—1983

TURMAN, Lawrence
   The Turman-Foster Co.
   Universal Studios, Bldg. 507
   Universal City, CA 91608
   Telephone: (213) 508-3182

credits: The Gift of Life *(as Executive Producer with David Foster)* (CBS)—1982

VALENTE, Renee
   Office: Twentieth Century-Fox TV
   10201 West Pico Boulevard
   Los Angeles, CA 90035
   Telephone: (213) 203-2012

credits: Contract on Cherry Street—1976, Blind Ambition—1979, Swan Song—1980, Jacqueline Susann's Valley of the Dolls—1981

VERTUE, Beryl
   Office: Chrystalis Group
   9225 West Sunset Blvd.
   Los Angeles, CA 90069
   Telephone: (213) 550-0171

credits: Parole (CBS)—1981

VON ZERNECK, Frank
   Business: Moonlight Productions, Inc.
   2029 Century Park East, Suite 4240
   Los Angeles, CA 90067
   Telephone: (213) 552-9455

credits: 21 Hours At Munich, Centerfold, Disaster on the Coastliner, Anatomy of a Seduction, Portrait of an Escort, Miracle on Ice *(with Robert Greenwald)*—1981, Return of the Rebels (CBS)—1981, Lois Gibbs and the Love Canal (CBS)—1982, In the Custody of Strangers (ABC)—1982

WEITZ, Barry
   Business: Barry Weitz Films
   8844 West Olympic Boulevard
   Beverly Hills, CA 90211
   Telephone: (213) 278-4015

credits: Strike Force—1975, Shark Kill—1976, She's Dressed to Kill—1979, Reunion—1980, Desperate Voyage—1980

WILLIAMS, Anson
Business: Anson Productions
11350 Ventura Blvd.
Studio City, CA 91604
Telephone: (213) 766-3896
credits: Skyward—1980

WIZAN, Joseph
(see also Producers)
Office: CBS Theatrical Films
Studio City, CA 90164
credits: The Two Worlds of Jennie Logan
(with Ron Samuels) (CBS)—19__ , The
Night of the Scarecrow (CBS)—1981

WOLPER, David
Business: The Wolper Organization
4000 Warner Boulevard

Burbank, CA 91522
Telephone: (213) 954-4000
credits: The 500 Pound Jerk—1973, The
Morning After—1974, Unwed Father—
1974, Men of the Dragon—1974, Get
Christie Love—1974, Death Stalk—1975,
Brenda Starr—1976, Roots (miniseries,
ABC)—1977, Roots: The Next Generations (miniseries, ABC)—1978, Moviola
(miniseries, NBC)—1979, The Thorn Birds
(miniseries, ABC)—1982

YELLEN, Linda
Agent: The Sy Fischer Co.
10100 Santa Monica Blvd., Suite 2440
Los Angeles, CA 90067
Telephone: (213) 557-0388
credits: Playing for Time—1980

PRODUCTION COMPANY EXECUTIVES
MOVIES FOR TELEVISION

production companies, movies for television

ABC CIRCLE FILMS
9911 West Pico Boulevard
Los Angeles, CA 90035
Tel.: (213) 557-6860
Brandon Stoddard—Senior Vice
President, ABC Entertainment
Herb Jellinek—President,
ABC Circle Films
Ted Butcher—Vice President, Film
Production for TV

CARSON PRODUCTIONS
4123 Radford Avenue
Studio City, CA 91604
Tel.: (213) 506-5333
John J. McMahon—President of Carson
Productions and Carson Films
Peter Palmer—Vice President of
Production and Development
Jerry Rubin—Vice President of Business
Affairs

DICK CLARK CINEMA PRODUCTIONS
3003 West Olive Avenue
Burbank, CA 91505
Tel.: (213) 841-3003
Dick Clark—President
Preston Fischer—Vice President,
Theatrical & TV Film Production
Jody B. Paonessa—Director of
Development
Fran La Maina—Executive Vice
President

COLUMBIA PICTURES TELEVISION
Columbia Plaza
Burbank, CA 91505
Tel.: (213) 954-6000
Herman Rush—President
Jonathan Azelrod—Senior Vice
President
Seymour Friedman—Senior Vice
President, Exec. Prod. Manager
Stephen Girard—Vice President,
Creative Affairs

Charles Schnebel—Vice President,
Current Programs
Christine Foster—Vice President
Movies of the Week
Charles Goldstein—Vice President,
Post Production
Michael Grossman—Vice President in
charge of Business Affairs
Deborah Cutler—Director, Literary
Affairs
Hans Proppe—Director, Movies of
the Week
Rachael Tabori—Director of Dramatic
Development
Joseph Indelli—Senior Vice President,
Domestic Syndication

COMWORLD PRODUCTIONS
(a Comworld Group Division)
15301 Ventura Blvd., Suite 230
Sherman Oaks, CA 91403
Tel.: (213) 907-1450
Alan Sloan—President
Deanne Barkley—Executive Producer
Philip Barry—Executive Producer
Robert Kosberg—Executive Producer
David Simon—Executive Producer
Matthew N. Herman—Vice President,
Production
James W. McCallum—Vice President,
Development, Syndication & Pay TV
*Gloria Monty Productions–Comworld
coventure:*
Charles A. Pratt—Head of Production
Marshal Backlar—Vice President,
Development

EMBASSY TELEVISION
100 Universal City Plaza
Universal City, CA 91608
Tel.: (213) 985-4321
Michael Grade—President
Al Burton—Executive Vice President,
Creative Affairs

production companies, movies for television

Virginia Carter—Senior Vice President,
Creative Affairs
Michael Weisbarth—Senior Vice
President, Programs
Glenn Padmick—Senior Vice President,
Current Programs
Barbara Brogliatti—Vice President of
Media, Publicity, Promotion and
Advertising
Jane Murray—Casting
Robert Berry—Vice President, Film
Production
Richard Clayman—Vice President, Tape
Production

EMI TV
9229 Sunset Boulevard, Penthouse
Los Angeles, CA 90069
Tel.: (213) 859-8250

Roger Gimbel—President
Paul Cameron—Vice President of
Production
Tony Converse—Vice President in
charge of Development
E. Jamie Schloss—Vice President,
Business Affairs

HANNA-BARBERA PRODUCTIONS
3400 Cahuenga Boulevard West
Los Angeles, CA 90068
Tel.: (213) 851-5000

Joseph Barbera—President
Margaret Loesch—Executive for
Creative Affairs and Production
Jack Mendelsohn—Developer-Producer
Executive
Hank Saroyan. Developer-Producer
Executive
Chris Bough—Developer-Producer
Executive
Bob Johnson—Developer-Producer
Executive
*The Richard Crenna Company is
affiliated with Hanna-Barbera Prod.
for development of movies for television
and series.*

HIGHGATE PRODUCTIONS *angela Costelo.*
1350 Sixth Avenue
New York, NY
Tel.: (212) 397-9710

William F. Deneen—President
Frank Doelger—Vice President,
Television
Roberta Becker—Director of
Development
Linda Gottlieb—Executive in charge of
Features

INTER PLANETARY PRODUCTIONS
14225 Ventura Blvd.
Sherman Oaks, CA 91423
Tel.: (213) 981-4950

Max Keller—Chairman
Micheline Keller—President
Patricia Herskovic—Executive Vice
President, Production
Ed Gold—Vice President, Development
Bert Gold—Executive in charge of
Production

JERRY LEIDER PRODUCTIONS
1041 North Formosa Avenue
Los Angeles, CA 90046
Tel.: (213) 650-2888

Jerry Leider—President
Robin Braun—Executive Story Editor
Joel Morwood—Executive in charge of
Production

LORIMAR TELEVISION
3970 Overland Avenue
Culver City, CA 90230
Tel.: (213) 202-2000

Merv Adelson—Chairman of the Board
Lee Rich—President
Bernard Weitzman—President,
Television Acquisitions
Edward O. Denault—Vice President of
Production (Film/TV)
Ken Page—President, TV Distribution

production companies, movies for television

Malcolm Stuart—Vice President, Movies/Movies of the Week/Mini-series
Joanne Brough—Vice President, Creative Affairs
Cindy Dunne—Vice President, TV Development
Bridget Potter—Vice President, Film and TV Development, New York
Robert Crutchfield—Vice President, Advertising and Publicity
Barbara Miller—Vice President, Casting
Michael Zucker—Vice President, Special Projects
Susan Dalsimer—Director of Development, East Coast

MARBLE ARCH PRODUCTIONS
12711 Ventura Blvd.
Studio City, CA 91604
Tel.: (213) 760-2110

Irwin Moss—President, Marble Arch Television
John Angier—Vice President, Business Affairs
Dennis Doty—Senior Vice President, Creative Affairs
Judy Polone—Vice President, Dramatic Programs
Ralph Rivera—Vice President, Chief Financial Officer
Howard Alston—Vice President, Production
Richard M. Ravin—Director, Story Department

METROMEDIA PRODUCERS CORP.
5746 Sunset Boulevard
Los Angeles, CA 90020
Tel.: (213) 462-7111

Robert Wood—President
Ethel Winant—Senior Vice President, Creative Affairs
James Stabile—Executive Vice President, MPC

Alan Silverbach—Executive Vice President for Worldwide Distribution
Herb Lazarus—Senior Vice President for Worldwide Distribution
Charles Raymond—Vice President of Production
Jay Wolpert—Vice President, Program Development
James Wethers—Vice President of Domestic Sales
Bill Doty—Director of Creative Services, Publiciy/Promotion

MGM TELEVISION
10202 West Washington Boulevard
Culver City, CA 90230
Tel.: (213) 558-5000

Thomas D. Tannenbaum—President
Werner Michel—Senior Vice President, Creative Affairs
Lloyd Weintraub—Director of Movies and Miniseries
Diana Dreiman—Vice President of Comedy Development
Ron Taylor—Vice President of Dramatic Programs
Virginia Hegge—
Dick Birne—Vice President of Production
Jerry Stanley—Vice President of Current Programs

MTM ENTERPRISES
4024 Radford Avenue
Studio City, CA 91604
Tel.: (213) 760-5000

Arthur Price—President
Mel Blumenthal—Executive Vice President, Business Affairs
Stuart Irwin—Executive Vice President, Creative Affairs
Abby Singer—Vice President, Production
Lawrence Bloustein—Vice President, Public Relations

Geri Windsor—Vice President, Talent
Tom Palmieri—Vice President,
Operations
Alan Bernard—Vice President, Live TV &
Special Projects

NEUFELD-DAVIS PRODUCTIONS
9454 Wilshire Boulevard, Suite 309
Beverly Hills, CA 90212
Tel.: (213) 858-2929

Mace Neufeld—President
John H. Levoff—President, Television
Division
John Orland—Production Executive
for Development
Thomas H. Brodek—Executive Vice
President, Film Production
Peter Exline—Director of Creative Affairs

PARAMOUNT TELEVISION
5555 Melrose Avenue
Los Angeles, CA 90038
Tel.: (213) 468-5000

Gary Nardino—President, Paramount
Pictures Television
Robert Rosenbaum—Senior Vice
President, Production
Richard Weston—Senior Vice President
of Business Affairs
Jeffrey Benson—Vice President of
Program Development
Mark Ovitz—Vice President, Current
Programming
Grant Rosenberg—Director, Drama
Programs and TV Movies
Karen Moore—Director, Drama
Programs and TV Movies

PLAYBOY PRODUCTIONS
8560 Sunset Blvd.
Los Angeles, CA 90069
Tel.: (213) 659-4080

W. Russel Barry—President

Tony Ford—Vice President, Creative
Affairs
David Lewine—Division Vice President,
Cable Television
Bob Shanks—Producer, Playboy Channel
Ann Shanks—Producer, Playboy Channel

POLYGRAM TELEVISION
3940 Overland Avenue
Culver City, CA 90230
Tel.: (213) 202-4400

Norman Horowitz—President
Seymour Berns—Vice President of
Production
Elizabeth Sykes—Director of
Co-productions & Development
(New York)
Brian Pike—Vice President of
Acquisitions and Development

QM PRODUCTIONS
10960 Wilshire Blvd.
Los Angeles, CA 90024
Tel.: (213) 208-2000

Jerry Golod—Vice President of
Programs
Ellen Schwartz—Vice President of
Program Development
Janet Saust-Krusi—Director of Program
Development
QM is a division of Taft Entertainment
Co.

RUTHLESS FILMS
10202 West Washington Blvd.
Culver City, CA 90230
Tel.: (213) 558-5462
Julia Phillips—President
Arlene Sidaris—Television Production
Harlan Goodman—Associate Producer
Judy Rohloff—Executive Assistant

production companies, movies for television

AARON SPELLING PRODUCTIONS
Warners Hollywood Studios
1041 N. Formosa Avenue
Los Angeles, CA 90046
Tel.: (213) 650-3991
Aaron Spelling—President
Douglas Cramer—Executive Vice
  President
Norman Henry—Vice President in
  charge of Production
Lyn Loring—Vice President in charge of
  Talent and Development
E. Duke Vincent—Supervising Producer
Tony Shepherd—Director of Series
  Development
Bret Garwood—Executive Coordinator

TEN-FOUR PRODUCTIONS
8271 Melrose Avenue
Los Angeles, CA 90046
Tel.: (213) 655-9470
Sam Strangis—President
Greg Strangis—Vice President

**TWENTIETH CENTURY-FOX
TELEVISION**
10201 West Pico Boulevard
Los Angeles, CA 90064
Tel.: (213) 277-2211
Harris Katleman—Chairman of the
  Board
Edward B. Gradinger—Group Executive
  Vice President and Chief Operating
  Officer
Andrea Baynes—Executive Vice
  President in charge of Production
Mark Evans—Vice President, Production
  Management
Peter Grad—Vice President,
  Development
Barry Lowen—Vice President and
  Executive in charge of Special
  Projects

Robert Morim—Executive Vice
  President, Worldwide Syndication
Lea Stalmaster—Vice President, Current
  Programs
Richard Rosetti—Vice President for
  Television Movies and Miniseries

UNITED ARTISTS TELEVISION
3910 Overland Avenue
Culver City, CA 90230
Tel.: (213) 202-0202
Richard Reisberg—President
Jerry Gottlieb—Executive Vice
  President
Andrew Siegel—Vice President,
  Creative Affairs

UNIVERSAL TELEVISION
100 Universal City Plaza
Universal City, CA 91608
Tel.: (213) 985-4321
Al Rush—President, MCA Television
  Group
Robert Harris—President
Burt Astor—Vice President, TV
  Production
Charles Engel—Executive Vice President
Kerry McCluggage—Vice President,
  Mini-series and Movies for TV

VIACOM PRODUCTIONS
CBS Studio Center
4024 Radford Avenue
Studio City, CA 91604
Tel.: (213) 760-5000
Sy Salkowitz—President
Leonard A. Rosenberg—Vice President,
  Development
Eric Veale—Vice President of Operations
Terry Morse, Jr.—Vice President of
  Production

WARNER BROS. TELEVISION
4000 Warner Boulevard
Burbank, CA 91522
Tel.: (213) 954-3027

Alan Shayne—President
Richard Korbitz—Senior Vice President
    of Production
Robert Doudell—Vice President and
    Executive Production Manager
Edward Bleier—Executive Vice
    President—East Coast
Elaine Cohen—Director of
    Programming—East Coast
Barry M. Meyer—Executive Vice
    President
Franklin Barton—Senior Vice President,
    Creative Affairs
David Sacks—Vice President, Current
    Programming
Charles McLain—Vice President,
    Miniseries and Movies for TV

TELEVISION NETWORK EXECUTIVES

television network executives

ABC ENTERTAINMENT
2040 Avenue of the Stars
Los Angeles, CA 90067
Telephone: (213) 557-7777

Anthony D. Thomopoulous—President
Brandon Stoddard—Senior Vice
President
Stu Samuels—Vice President, Motion
Pictures for Television
Jud Kinberg—Executive Producer,
Motion Pictures for Television
Dottie Gagliano—Director of Creative
Services, Motion Pictures and Novels
for Television
Herbert Jellinek—Vice President,
Production
Ilene Amy Berg—Executive Producer,
Motion Pictures for Television
Lewis H. Erlicht—Senior Vice President,
Prime Time Series
Michael Sullivan—Director of Comedy
Development

CBS ENTERTAINMENT
CBS Television City
7800 Beverly Boulevard
Los Angeles, CA 90036
Tel.: (213) 852-2345

B. Donald Grant—President
Harvey Shephard—Vice President,
Programs
Steve Mills—Vice President, Motion
Pictures for Television and Miniseries
Kim LeMasters—Vice President,
Program Development and Production
Robert M. Silberling—Vice President
in charge of Telefilms
Scott Siegler—Vice President, Comedy
Program Development
Arnold Burstin—Vice President of
Business Affairs for Motion Pictures
for Television and Miniseries
George Berntsen—Vice President of
Feature Films and Late Night
Program Planning
Bernie Sofronski—Vice President of
Special Programs
William B. Klein—Vice President of

Business Affairs
Steve Berman—Director, Comedy
Program Development
Carla Singer—Vice President, Dramatic
Program Development
Mark Waxman—Director, Dramatic
Program Development
Stan Hough—Director of Motion Pictures
and Miniseries

NBC TELEVISION
NBC ENTERTAINMENT
West Coast Offices:
NBC-Burbank Television Center
3000 West Alameda Boulevard
Burbank, CA 91532:
Tel.: (213) 840-4444

Grant Tinker—Chairman of the Board
and Chief Executive Officer
Robert Mulholland—President and
Chief Operating Officer
Irwin Segelstein—Vice Chairman of
the Board
Ray Timothy—Vice President,
NBC Network
Brandon Tartikoff—President of
NBC Entertainment
Perry Lafferty—Senior Vice President,
Programs and Talent
Joan Barnett—Vice President, Motion
Pictures for TV
Patrick Betz—Vice President,
Story Department
Hamilton Cloud—Vice President,
Current Comedy
Charles Goldstein—Vice President of
Film Production
Warren Littlefield—Vice President of
Development
Josh Kane—Vice President, Theatrical
Features (New York)
Marian Seringer—Vice President
Literary Affairs (New York)
Perry Massey—Vice President,
Program Production
Michele Brustin—Drama Development
Susan Baerwald—Director, Miniseries
and Novels of TV
Karen Danaher—Director, Motion
Pictures for TV
Allen Sabinson—Director, Motion
Pictures for TV